Contents

Introduction

Salads are a timeless dish that span across many cultures and cuisines. They are also ever-evolving. A salad, according to the Oxford dictionary, is "a cold dish of various mixtures of raw or cooked vegetables, usually seasoned with oil, vinegar, or other dressing, and sometimes accompanied by meat, fish, or other ingredients" What's your definition of a salad? Do you think of a plate of good, healthy, nutritious food, full of vibrant colour and crunch? Or does the word salad make you conjure up images of limp, watery lettuce coupled with slimy cucumber and overripe tomatoes? The latter will certainly not get your salivary juices flowing!

If you want to start including more salads in your diet, but are not exactly excited at the thought, then change what a salad means to you. A salad can be anything you want it to be! The list of potential ingredients is endless and you can be as creative as you want, using ingredients you enjoy. For example, replace the lettuce with kale, swap the tomatoes and cucumber for roasted peppers and courgettes, throw in some warm mixed beans and before you know it you have a yummy bean salad on your plate... it's as easy as that!

POCKET COUNTER

- ★ Over 750 photos
- ★ Great accompaniment to the **CARB & CALORIE COUNTER**
- ★ Perfect when out and about!

FLASHCARDS

- ★ 54 cards in each pack
- ★ Range of popular food & drinks
- ★ Perfect educational tool

MOBILE APP

Available for iPhone & Android

- ★ Over 3,500 photos of popular food & drinks
- ★ Perfect for weight loss, portion control & diabetes
- ★ The ultimate portable calorie counter!

PLUS...
FREE HEALTH RESOURCES

FREE!

- ★ Register for FREE access to 30 PDF resources
- ★ www.carbsandcals.com/register

Visit www.carbsandcals.com

Carbs & Cals SALADS

80 healthy salad recipes plus 350 ingredient photos to create your own!

1ST EDITION

First published in Great Britain in 2016
by Chello Publishing Limited

Registered Company Number 7237986

www.chellopublishing.co.uk | info@chellopublishing.co.uk

With special thanks to: Fran Turner, George Malache, Gian Mizzi, Justine Rose, Maxine Gregory, Rayyah McCaul, Simon Callaghan, Victoria Francis, Warren Thorpe, Yoshi Gray.

The information contained in this book is not a substitute for medical or other professional guidance. Please consult your GP before making any alterations to medications or changing medical treatment. Although all reasonable care has been taken in the writing of this book, the authors and publisher are not responsible for any specific health needs; they do not accept any legal responsibility or liability for any personal injury or other consequences, damage or loss arising from any use of information and advice contained within this book.

The authors have asserted their moral rights.

ISBN: 978-1-908261-18-2 Printed in Malta 0416

Authors	Chris Cheyette BSc (Hons) MSc RD
	Yello Balolia BA (Hons)
Recipes by	Chris Cheyette BSc (Hons) MSc RD
	Victoria Francis BSc (Hons) RD
Photography	Simon Callaghan & Francesca Turner
Design Concept	George F Malache
Graphic Design	Maxine Gregory BA (Hons)
Additional Layout	Yello Balolia BA (Hons)
Introduction Text	Victoria Francis BSc (Hons) RD

For more information, please visit:
www.carbsandcals.com

Salads are versatile, portable, require minimal preparation, are simple to make and can be adapted to suit all four seasons of the year. Many wouldn't choose a bowl of stew in the summer, but a warm hearty salad of roasted vegetables and chorizo would be a perfect dish on a cold winter's night. They are, in fact, very versatile and can be included in ALL healthy eating diet plans, including the portfolio diet for lowering cholesterol, low carbohydrate diets, weight loss plans such as the 5:2 or 800 calorie blood sugar diet, and the now popular Meat Free Mondays.

However, don't get carried away thinking the pesto pasta pot or cheese salad from your local supermarket is a good salad option... With a few 'wrong choices' an honest, innocent, healthy salad can quickly become a 'dirty salad'. A homemade salad with a rainbow of vegetables, some lean protein and grains is an excellent nutritious meal choice. Replacing this with a supermarket pasta pot, smothered in mayonnaise or pesto, can treble the fat content and vastly reduce the nutritional quality.

If you want to lose weight, eat a more nutritious diet, or boost your fibre intake, then salads and you need to become good friends. This book aims to show you how salads can be incorporated into any healthy eating meal plan, and together with evidence-based nutrition facts and recipes, help to inspire you to reach your dietary goal.

Health benefits of salads

Reach your 5-a-day

Scientific evidence strongly supports the role of fruit and vegetables in our diet to reduce the risk of developing diseases such as heart disease and cancer. Current UK dietary advice suggests to consume at least 5 portions of fruit and vegetables a day, a recommendation that is supported by official guidance from the World Health Organisation, who recommend a minimum of 400g fruit and vegetables a day. This amount is actually the minimum, based on what is likely to be achieved, and yet research shows that a third of adults do not meet these recommendations.

Page
86

5
5-a-day

Pear & Pomegranate
Salad

Blueberries
40g

½
5-a-day

1
5-a-day

Cucumber
80g

5
5-a-day

Page
83

Roast Veg Satay
Salad

Each of the following counts
as 1 portion of your 5-a-day:

★ 80g fresh, frozen or tinned
   fruit or vegetables
★ 30g dried fruit
★ 150ml pure, unsweetened
   fruit or vegetable juice
★ 80g beans and pulses

Using a rainbow of vegetables and
fruit in your salads will provide you
with a wide variety of nutrients
(including vitamins A and C), fibre,
phytonutrients and antioxidants, all
of which will nourish your body and
reduce the risk of health problems.

Ten of the salad recipes in this
book contain all 5 of your 5-a-day.

Want to mix it up a little?

Check out our
smoothie book
for more ideas on
tasty and inventive
ways to reach your
5-a-day in one hit!

5
5-a-day

Increase your fibre intake

There is strong evidence that associates an increase in total fibre intake (especially cereal grains and whole grains) with a lower risk of heart disease, type 2 diabetes and bowel cancer. Fibre also has a role in lowering cholesterol levels and controlling blood sugar levels. Soluble fibre, found in fruit and vegetables, is also known to slow down digestion, which helps us feel fuller for longer. These benefits have led the Scientific Advisory Committee on Nutrition to update fibre intake recommendations to 30g per day for adults (the current average intake is 19g per day). With an average vegetable portion containing 1-3g fibre, salads can play an important role in boosting your fibre intake and promoting good bowel health. The addition of nuts, seeds, pulses and/or grains will further boost the fibre content and keep you feeling nicely satisfied for longer.

3g Fibre

Lentils
80g

19g Fibre

Page
94

Avocado
70g

3g Fibre

Three Bean &
Tomato Salad

Boost your sources of protein

Protein is made up of amino acids, the building blocks for muscles, and is essential for the repair and growth of body cells. It is also vital in keeping our immune system strong. All protein, including meat, chicken, fish, eggs, cheese, pulses, nuts and seeds, can be added to salads to increase the nutritional quality and aid with satiety (feeling of fullness).

The Department of Health has recently advised that people who eat more than 90g (cooked weight) of red and processed meat a day, should ideally cut down to 70g per day (or 500g per week), due to a link between processed meat and an increased risk of bowel cancer. Consequently, for both health and environmental reasons, there is a big move towards using more plant-based proteins like beans, soya, tofu, nuts, seeds and grains such as quinoa instead. Eating more oily fish will also help to boost your intake of omega-3 oils and reduce your consumption of saturated fats. This book provides you with ideas on how to include more of these plant-based proteins in your diet, with less reliance on proteins from red and processed meat.

16g
Protein

King
Prawns
100g

11g
Protein

Soya
Beans 80g

20g
Protein

Page
84

Thai Vegan
Salad

Pack your plate with low-calorie foods

You can get a lot for your money when it comes to fruit and vegetables as they are low in calories and a great source of fibre. This makes them an obvious choice when trying to lower your calorie intake. Due to the wide variety of vegetables used, each salad in this book contains less than 500 calories, giving you a wide range of lunch and evening meal ideas to choose from.

18 Cals
Cherry Tomatoes 80g

Page 40
90 Cals
Bittersweet Grapefruit Treat Salad

18 Cals
Yellow Pepper 80g

Raw Beetroot 40g
14 Cals

Lambs Lettuce 20g
3 Cals

Carrot 40g
14 Cals

Stay heart healthy with good fats

Fat gets a bad name in the press, but we need it in our diet as it is a major component of our cell membranes. It provides us with insulation and is needed for the absorption of certain nutrients such as vitamins A and D. What is key, is the *type* of fat; shift your focus to the good fats, namely mono- and polyunsaturated fats, as these have a positive effect on our health. Recipes including olive oil and avocado provide an excellent source of monounsaturated fat; while oily fish and some seeds (including linseeds and chia seeds) offer a rich source of omega-3s, which are known to be protective against heart disease.

Mustard Chicken Salad

Page 101

11g Fat

Berry Pecan Cheese Salad

34g Fat

Page 74

Smoked Mackerel 75g

18g Fat

Ingredient Health Benefits

Avocado

A rich source of monounsaturated fat, which is beneficial to heart health

Broccoli

High in vitamin K, which helps wounds heal properly

Carrots

High in vitamin A, which helps protect the eyes and assists with vision in low light

Parsnip

Source of iron, important for preventing anaemia

Spinach

Rich in magnesium, which helps to calm the body and relax muscles

Tomato

Contains lycopene, an antioxidant known to protect against heart disease

Beetroot

High in potassium, lowering blood pressure

Butternut Squash

Low in calories and high in fibre, ideal for weight loss plans

Kale

A source of folate, needed for healthy blood and brain function

Red Cabbage

High in vitamin K, for maintaining bone strength and health

Sweet Potato

Fibre-rich and a source of slow releasing energy

Yellow Pepper

High in beta-carotene (which makes vitamin A) to avoid an itchy scalp and dry hair

Blueberries
An excellent source of cancer-fighting antioxidants

Figs
Contain prebiotics to promote a healthy digestive system

Dried Apricots
Great non-dairy source of calcium, needed for bone and dental health

Mango
Contains immune-boosting vitamin A

Almonds
Heart-healthy due to their high vitamin E content

Cashews
Good source of zinc, essential for enhancing memory and thinking skills

Hazelnuts
Their high vitamin E content makes them great for healthy skin

Walnuts
Anti-inflammatory, so great for those suffering with joint pain and arthritis

Egg
A good source of high-quality protein and B-vitamins

Salmon
High in omega-3 fatty acids, helping to reduce the risk of heart disease

Prawns
A low-calorie source of protein to keep you feeling full

Sardines
High in vitamin D, beneficial to keep bones healthy

Salads as part of your diet plan

What is a healthy, balanced diet and how can salads be included?

The benefits of a healthy, balanced diet include a reduced risk of long-term conditions such as cancer and heart disease, an improvement in general health and wellbeing, as well as a better ability to monitor and maintain weight. To achieve a healthy weight, a balanced diet should contain appropriate portions of a variety of nutrient rich foods, such as:

★ Fruit and vegetables for antioxidants, vitamins and minerals

★ Dairy foods, such as milk and yogurt, for calcium

★ Wholegrain carbohydrates, such as oats, pearl barley and puy lentils, for B vitamins and fibre

★ Meat, fish, nuts, eggs and quinoa for good quality protein

★ Oily fish and nuts for omega-3 oils

Salads can contribute greatly towards a balanced diet because of the extensive range of nutrient dense foods they often include. With so many different salad recipes to choose from, who said healthy eating should be boring?!

Different diets work for different people.

The key to achieving success in reaching your goal involves finding an approach that works for you and your lifestyle, and one you can stick to. Salads can be low in calories and also provide a nutrient rich option that can be incorporated into many different eating plans.

Chilli Prawn & Beansprout Salad

5:2 diet

The 5:2 diet involves 5 days of normal eating and 2 days of fasting. When on a 500 calorie fast day, high protein, or high fibre meal choices are key, as protein and fibre are known to keep you feeling full and satisfied until your next meal. Our *Chilli Prawn & Beansprout* salad packs a protein punch of 16g, but only 115 calories, making it a perfect lunchtime choice! Or choose the *Roasted Winter Warmer* salad for dinner, which contains 270 calories, 12g fibre (⅓ of your target) and all 5 of your 5-a-day, even on a fast day! Please see page 23 about how to incorporate salads into your 5:2 diet plan.

Page
43

115
Cals

5:2 Diet Photos
To buy your copy, visit:
www.carbsandcals.com/5-2

Very low-calorie diet

Very low-calorie diets (less than 800 calories per day) have been used successfully in clinical practice for many years to achieve weight loss. Recent evidence shows that adhering to an 800 calorie diet for 8 weeks causes significant weight loss and reversal of abnormally high blood sugars. Following a very low-calorie diet means every mouthful has to pack a nutritious punch and fill you up if you are going to stick to it. Salads are the perfect choice! Classic salad ingredients, such as vegetables, are low in calories; while lean proteins such as eggs, and fibre rich pulses such as chickpeas, will keep you feeling full until your next meal. Our *Warm Squash & Houmous* salad would be an ideal dinner choice as it contains only 320 calories, but 14g protein and 12g fibre. As an added bonus, it also provides 3½ of your 5-a-day!

320 Cals

Warm Squash & Houmous Salad

Page **93**

Page **41**

95 Cals

Herbed Triple Tomato Salad

Low-carb diets

These diets are popular amongst people who want to lose weight, and also those with diabetes who have to manage their blood glucose levels. There are over 36 salads in this book containing less than 20g carbs and 10 salads with less than 10g carbs, so they're an ideal choice when looking to keep your carbohydrate intake low. Our *King Prawn & Avocado* salad contains only 6g carbs, but provides a whopping 18g protein and 3 of your 5-a-day fruit & veg!

King Prawn & Avocado Salad

6g Carbs

Page **34**

High-protein diets

Protein, as already stated, is the nutrient that keeps us feeling fuller for longer and has minimal impact on blood glucose levels. Research has shown that we are unable to utilise much more than 20g protein at any one time, so try to aim for above this amount in each main meal. Our *Mango Chicken & Salsa* salad would be ideal, providing 39g protein in under 250 calories; a perfect lunchtime meal to keep those mid-afternoon munchies at bay!

Mango Chicken & Salsa Salad

39g Protein

Page **98**

High-fibre diets

The average UK adult currently consumes 19g fibre per day, so the new recommendation of 30g may feel unachievable for many. The inclusion of beans, grains and pulses, such as lentils and chickpeas, will make this easier. Choosing our *Roasted Roots & Lentils* salad will provide you with 17g fibre in one go and all 5 of your 5-a-day!

Roasted Roots & Lentils Salad

17g Fibre

Page **96**

Salads for people with diabetes

Diabetes is a condition where the glucose levels in the blood are too high because the body cannot use the glucose properly. The two main types of diabetes are type 1 and type 2.

Type 1 diabetes develops because the immune system attacks and destroys the cells that produce insulin, which leads to high blood glucose levels. It is treated with insulin via an injection or pump. For those with type 1 diabetes who adjust their insulin dose according to their carb intake, salads can be included in their diet as long as the carb content is calculated and matched with quick acting insulin.

PLEASE NOTE: The carbs displayed with each salad are the total carbs from all ingredients, including vegetables, pulses and grains. When calculating an insulin dose, some will need to subtract the carb content of certain foods (such as vegetables and pulses). For further guidance on how to count the carbs in a salad and match with quick acting insulin, speak with your diabetes dietitian or nurse specialist.

Type 2 diabetes develops when the pancreas does not produce enough insulin, or the body is unable to use the insulin effectively (known as insulin resistance). Type 2 diabetes can primarily be treated with a healthy diet and lifestyle change, such as increased physical activity. It is, however, a progressive condition, and many people may need to commence medication at some point to control their blood glucose levels.

For most people with type 2 diabetes, weight loss is the primary goal to reduce insulin resistance and improve insulin sensitivity. Emerging evidence supports the short-term use of very low-calorie diets (800 calories per day) to reverse insulin resistance and type 2 diabetes in some people. Because of their high fibre content and low energy density, salads play a pivotal role in such weight loss diets.

If you have diabetes and are taking medication (including insulin), speak with your healthcare professional for guidance on losing weight and how to include salads in your daily diet.

How to use this book

This book includes 80 carefully-created salad recipes, divided into the following sections:

Low-carb Pages **28 - 37**

7g Carbs

Low-calorie Pages **38 - 47**

145 Cals

General recipes Pages **48 - 77**

5 5-a-day

240 Cals

5-a-day Pages **78 - 87**

10g Fibre

High-fibre Pages **88 - 97**

23g Protein

High-protein Pages **98 - 107**

Within each section, the salads are listed in calorie order, starting with the lowest calorie recipe. For each salad, the nutritional information for the following nutrients are clearly displayed in colour coded circles:

Cals 5-a-day Fibre SatFat Fat Protein Carbs

Simply browse the variety of recipes and select ones that meet your dietary goal.

Alternative dressing recipes are provided at the end of the salads section of the book, each listing the nutritional information per serving.

A few things to note:

★ The recipes use average/medium sizes of vegetables and fruit, and weights shown are for the edible part (after being peeled or stoned), unless otherwise stated.

★ Some recipes use a handy measure (e.g. large handful of watercress) instead of a specific weight. Should you wish to know the exact weights, simply find that portion in the ingredients section. For example, the *Broad Bean & Feta* salad on page 89 uses 1 large handful of watercress. Looking at watercress on page 132, you will see that 1 large handful weighs 20g.

Beetroot
(raw) 80g

260 Cals

Page **89**

1g Protein

0g Fat

0g Fibre

0g Carbs

4 Cals

0 5-a-day

Watercress
20g, large handful

Broad Bean
& Feta Salad

★ Each salad displays the calorie saving if you leave off the dressing. This gives you greater control over your calorie intake, allowing you to omit the dressing or choose an alternative. Please note that the savings only include the calories, carbohydrate and fat where appropriate (the protein, saturated fat or fibre values are not included).

40 Cals

Lemon Dill Dressing

Leave off dressing to save:
75 Cals   4g Fat

★ Not all the recipes include salt and pepper, so adding such seasoning is down to personal taste. Such addition will not affect the calorie content.

★ The recipes use a mix of uncooked and cooked weights for rice, pasta, couscous, quinoa and pearl barley. The table below outlines the simple conversion for uncooked and cooked weights, although please bear in mind that the longer you cook your pasta and rice, the more water it absorbs, which can affect the final weight of the cooked product.

	Uncooked Weight	Cooked Weight
Couscous	35g	80g
Dried Pasta	45g	100g
Pearl Barley	25g	80g
Quinoa	30g	80g
Rice	35g	100g

Anchovy Shroom Pasta Salad

295 Cals

Page 57

Pearl Barley 80g

White Fusilli Pasta 100g

Creating your own recipes

The potential salad combinations are endless, so why not get creative? Try making up your own from the list of ingredients at the back of this book (pages 112 to 171). The nutritional content of each individual ingredient is shown, giving you the flexibility to create salad recipes to meet your own personal dietary goal. Again, it's worth writing down the details of your creations so you have a record of nutritional information and can make the recipe again in future.

6g Protein

6g Fat

4g SatFat

0g Fibre

Halloumi
25g

0g Carbs

78 Cals

0 5-a-day

1g Protein

0g Fat

1g Fibre

Mixed Salad Leaves
40g

1g Carbs

4 Cals

½ 5-a-day

0g Protein

0g Fat

1g Fibre

Blueberries
40g

4g Carbs

16 Cals

½ 5-a-day

My salad

Salad Leaves 40g (4 cals)

Halloumi 25g (78 cals)

Blueberries 40g (16 cals)

TOTAL = 98 cals

Making a 5:2 diet meal plan

The 5:2 approach enables you to lose weight without constant deprivation. Eating a normal, healthy diet 5 days a week and fasting on the 2 remaining days reduces your overall calorie intake and has proven to be an effective achievable method of weight loss for many people.

Here is an example of how to include salad into your fasting day:

1. Decide how you would like to split your calorie allowance for the day. For example, your 500 calories could be made up of two, or three meals, spread throughout the day:
   ★ 200 cals for brunch
   ★ 300 cals for dinner

2. Browse this book and decide which salad meets your dietary needs. If you normally get hungry mid-afternoon, you may want to have a high protein salad at lunch to keep you feeling satisfied and energised throughout the afternoon, or alternatively, you may prefer a small, light salad at lunch to allow for a larger evening meal.

3. Use this book alongside our Smoothies book and 5:2 Diet Photos book, to make your fasting days feel like a feast, not a famine!

Daily meal plan:

Brunch:

210 Cals

3 5-a-day

The Apricotty Smoothie

Dinner:

305 Cals

2 5-a-day

Page **35**

Leek, Egg & Bacon Salad

Total: **515** Cals   **5** 5-a-day

Producing a meal plan for a 1500 calorie diet

Fad diets, which promise quick weight loss results, are hard to follow for many people and the long-term data shows that the weight often doesn't stay off when a normal diet is resumed. Following a 1500 calorie diet plan can help you lose around 1/2kg (1lb) a week (more if you have lots to lose), without feeling that you are depriving yourself of everything.

Salads are a great way to ensure you meet your nutrient needs, such as reaching your 5-a-day and boosting your fibre intake, whilst limiting your calorie intake.

Example daily meal plan:

★ Breakfast: *Morning Glory* smoothie – 375 cals

Mid-morning snack: 5-spice popcorn – 90 cals

★ Lunch: *Walnut, Ham & Stilton* salad with 50g ciabatta – 490 cals

★ Mid-afternoon snack: Skinny cappuccino and nectarine – 120 cals

★ Dinner: *Creamy Prawn Orzo* salad – 415 cals

Total: 1,490 cals

Walnut, Ham & Stilton Salad

Page
62

355
Cals

For information on weight loss and working out your calorie target, visit:
www.carbsandcals.com/BMI

Choosing the right dressing

The basic components of salads (namely vegetables, fruit, lean proteins and grains) make them an obvious healthy choice. But the nutrients don't just stop with the salad ingredients... dressings can be another way to boost the nutritional content. Many salad dressings in the book use olive oil, known to be a rich source of antioxidants and high in the 'good' fats. Alternatively, using an avocado based dressing can further boost your vitamin A and fibre intake.

When it comes to both nutrition and taste, a dressing can make or break a salad. A lime and ginger dressing, for example, will add a zing to your plate adding only a few calories; while a creamy, salty blue cheese dressing, which works well against the bitter flavour of watercress, will significantly bump up your calorie intake.

Each salad in this book is made with a suggested dressing, chosen to complement the salad ingredients. However, there are also additional salad dressings that you can use to customise your salad to your taste preference, and of course, calorie requirements. Keep in mind, this will alter the overall nutritional and calorie content of the salad.

5 Cals

Mexican Flame
Dressing

60 Cals

Sweet & Spicy
Dressing

125 Cals

Blueberry Blast
Dressing

When including salads as part of a weight loss plan, use a small amount of dressing to keep calories down, or simply don't use one. When making your own dressings, you'll soon realise how many additional calories a 'little drizzle' can add!

Buying ingredients

★ It is best to use wholegrain pasta and rice to boost fibre content.

★ Use extra virgin olive oil for dressings where possible.

★ The thickness of shop bought tahini paste can vary, so you may wish to add more water to achieve the desired consistency.

★ Always use fresh, ripe fruit and vegetables.

★ Try to use organic produce where possible.

★ To keep the cost down, choose vegetables and fruit that are in season. Alternatively, you can replace one vegetable with another that is in season, but be mindful this may change the nutritional content.

★ A great way to add variety to your diet and ensure you always have your salad ingredients to hand is to order a fruit and vegetable box. Each delivery is different so you never know what salad recipe will be on the menu!

To see our recommended veg box companies, please visit:

www.carbsandcals.com/vegbox

Cooking Glossary

Blanch: Briefly cook vegetables in boiling water to seal in flavour and colour.

Drizzle: Pour the salad dressing evenly over the salad.

Flake: Use a fork, or hand, to break cooked fish into smaller pieces and to check if the fish is cooked. If cooked, the fish flesh should fall away easily.

Matchstick: Cut into thin strips.

Mince: Chopped very finely.

Parboil: Boil ingredient until it is partially cooked.

Ribboned: Vegetables shaved into ribbons using a peeler. If you have a spiralizer, this would work just as well.

Sauté: From the French verb, sauter, meaning 'to jump'. Sautéed food is cooked in a small amount of fat in an open pan on a high heat.

Segment: Divide citrus fruit into smaller sections.

Thinly sliced: Slice ingredient into thin slices using a sharp knife or spiralizer.

Toasted nuts: Nuts heated in a medium-hot frying pan to bring out the richness and flavour (without the addition of oil). Toast for a couple of minutes until fragrant, or light brown in colour.

Summer Sprouty Salmon

Super light and refreshing with only 140 calories

Ingredients

1 clove	**Garlic** (minced)
20g	**Alfalfa Sprouts**
¼	**Lemon** (juice only)
40g	**Petit Pois** (cooked)
⅓	**Courgette** (ribboned)
2 handfuls	**Lambs Lettuce**
50g	**Smoked Salmon** (strips)

Preparation

1. Combine **all the ingredients** except the salmon.
2. Lay the **salmon** on top of the salad and season with pepper.

140 Cals

2 5-a-day

3g Fibre

1g SatFat

5g Fat

17g Protein

6g Carbs

Size
Large
230g

Recipe Tip
We recommend using wild or organically farmed salmon to cut down the environmental impact

Feta & Pomegranate

Salty, zingy flavours to perk up your taste buds

Ingredients

1/3	**Red Onion** (wedges)
80g	**Aubergine** (cubed)
1 tsp	**Olive Oil**
1 tbsp	**Pomegranate Seeds** (heaped)
5	**Mint** leaves (chopped)
1	handful **Rocket**
25g	**Feta** (crumbled)

Dressing

1/4	**Lemon** (juice only)
1 tsp	**Olive Oil** (extra virgin)

Preparation

1. Roast the **onion** and **aubergine** with the **oil** at 180°C for 20 mins.
2. Whisk the **dressing**.
3. Combine **all the ingredients** with the dressing and serve.

| 9g Carbs | 6g Protein | 14g Fat | 5g SatFat | 4g Fibre | | 2 5-a-day | 185 Cals |

Nutrition Fact
Pomegranate is a good source of fibre and vitamin C

Leave off dressing to save: **35 Cals** **4g Fat**

Size
Small
180g

Tomozza Basil

This simple and tasty Italian classic is a great low-carb option

Ingredients

200g	**Beef Tomato**	(sliced)
50g	**Mozzarella**	(torn)
12	**Basil** leaves	(torn)
8	**Olives**	(small, chopped)

Dressing

1 tsp **Olive Oil** (extra virgin)

Preparation

1. Arrange the **tomato slices** on a plate and top with the **mozzarella**, **basil** and **olives**.

2. Finish with **olive oil**, salt & pepper.

220 Cals

1½ 5-a-day

3g Fibre

8g SatFat

17g Fat

11g Protein

6g Carbs

Size
Small
285g

Leave off dressing to save:
35 Cals   4g Fat

Nutrition Fact
Tomatoes contain the antioxidant lycopene

Steak & Sprouts

A perfect combination of steak, olives and sprouts

Ingredients

1 tsp	**Olive Oil**
100g	**Beef Sirloin** (raw, lean)
2	**Tomatoes** (small, chopped)
1	large handful **Watercress**
8	**Olives** (small, chopped)
1 sprig	**Dill** (finely chopped)
40g	**Alfalfa Sprouts**
¼	**Lemon** (juice only)

Preparation

1. Heat the **oil** in a pan over a medium-high heat and fry the **steak** for 2 mins each side. Remove the pan from heat.

2. Mix **all the salad ingredients** (except the lemon juice) and place on a plate.

3. Slice the steak into strips, and lay on top of the salad.

4. Drizzle with juices from the pan and the **lemon juice**.

3g	26g	12g	3g	3g
Carbs	Protein	Fat	SatFat	Fibre

2 5-a-day

225 Cals

Recipe Tip
Grow sprouts at home for a fresh and ready supply

Size
Medium
285g

Tuna & Dill Niçoise

A classic tuna salad with a refreshing dill and lemon dressing

Ingredients

2	handfuls **Rocket**
1 tbsp	**Capers**
100g	**Tuna** (tinned)
1	**Egg** (hard boiled, halved)
8	**Cherry Tomatoes** (halved)

Dressing

¼	**Lemon** (juice only)
1 sprig	**Dill** (chopped)
2 tsp	**Natural Yogurt** (fat free)

Preparation

1. Lay a bed of **rocket** on a plate and top with the **other salad ingredients**.
2. Combine the **dressing** and drizzle over the salad.

225 Cals

1 5-a-day

2g Fibre

2g SatFat

7g Fat

36g Protein

3g Carbs

Size
Medium
265g

Nutrition Fact
Tinned tuna is low in calories but high in protein

Mushroom Bacon Combo

Bacon and mushrooms with a splash of balsamic make this a hearty low-carb winner

Ingredients

80g	**Chestnut Mushrooms**	(sliced)
8	**Cherry Tomatoes**	(halved)
2	**Back Bacon**	rashers
1 tbsp	**Pine Nuts**	(toasted)
1/6	**Red Onion**	(thinly sliced)
1	handful **Spinach**	
1	handful **Rocket**	
2 sprigs	**Parsley**	

Dressing

2 tsp **Balsamic Vinegar**

Preparation

1. Griddle the **mushrooms**, **tomatoes** and **bacon**. Once cooked, slice the bacon.

2. In another pan, toast the **pine nuts**.

3. Arrange **all ingredients** on a plate and top with the bacon and pine nuts.

4. Add a splash of **balsamic vinegar** to finish.

9g Carbs	13g Protein	15g Fat	3g SatFat	3g Fibre	2½ 5-a-day	230 Cals

Recipe Tip
Toasting pine nuts intensifies their rich, irresistible flavour

Leave off dressing to save: 15 Cals · 4g Carbs

Size
Medium
240g

King Prawn & Avocado

Sweet pineapple and salty olives make for a great combination

Ingredients

¼	**Avocado** (cubed)
1 sprig	**Dill** (finely chopped)
8	**Olives** (small, halved)
40g	**Pineapple** (chopped)
1	**Spring Onion** (sliced)
100g	**King Prawns** (cooked)
2 sprigs	**Parsley** (finely chopped)
40g	**Little Gem Lettuce**
8	**Cherry Tomatoes** (quartered)

Dressing

¼	**Lemon** (juice only)
1 tsp	**Olive Oil** (extra virgin)

Preparation

1. Mix **all the salad ingredients** together, except the lettuce.
2. Whisk the **dressing** until well combined and stir through the salad.
3. Lay a bed of **lettuce** on a plate and top with salad mixture.

230 Cals

3 5-a-day

4g Fibre

3g SatFat

14g Fat

18g Protein

6g Carbs

Size
Medium
355g

Leave off dressing to save:
35 Cals   4g Fat

Nutrition Fact
Avocados are a rich source of monounsaturated fat

Leek, Egg & Bacon

A great weekend brunch alternative to a traditional fry-up

Ingredients

2	**Back Bacon** rashers
1 clove	**Garlic** (finely chopped)
80g	**Leeks** (sliced)
1 tsp	**Butter**
1	**Egg** (hard boiled, quartered)
40g	**Little Gem Lettuce**
40g	**Roasted Red Pepper** (from jar, sliced)

Dressing

½ tsp	**Dijon Mustard**
1 tsp	**White Wine Vinegar**
1 tsp	**Olive Oil** (extra virgin)

Preparation

1. Dry fry the **bacon** and set aside.
2. Using the same pan, fry the **garlic** and **leeks** in **butter**.
3. Chop the bacon and mix back in with the leeks, adding the **egg** and **pepper**.
4. Spoon the mixture onto a layer of **lettuce**.
5. Whisk the **dressing** and drizzle over the salad.

6g Carbs	19g Protein	23g Fat	8g SatFat	4g Fibre	2 5-a-day	305 Cals

Nutrition Fact
Leeks are thought to have a protective role against cancer

Leave off dressing to save:
40 Cals   4g Fat

Size
Medium
255g

Tofu & All The Greens

Crispy tofu with healthy greens make
this a light, refreshing choice

Ingredients

1 tsp	**Soy Sauce**
1 tsp	**Sesame Oil**
100g	**Tofu** (firm, cubed)
½	**Avocado** (cubed)
40g	**Soya Beans** (cooked)
⅛	**Cucumber** (matchsticks)
1	large handful **Watercress**
¼	**Lime** (juice only)
½ tsp	**Sesame Seeds**

Preparation

1. Dry **tofu** between paper towels to remove excess moisture.
2. Rub the **soy sauce** and **oil** onto the tofu and bake at 200°C for 45 mins.
3. Combine the **avocado** with the **soya beans**, **cucumber** and **watercress**.
4. Place the baked tofu on top of the salad, with a squeeze of **lime juice**.
5. Sprinkle with **sesame seeds**.

320 Cals	2 5-a-day		6g Fibre	5g SatFat	25g Fat	15g Protein	7g Carbs

Size
Medium
270g

Recipe Tip
Choose 'firm' or 'extra firm' tofu for that golden crispy crust

Egg & Mackerel Kicker

A creamy horseradish hit for the taste buds

Ingredients

2	handfuls **Mixed Salad Leaves**
40g	**Asparagus Tips** (blanched)
4	**Cherry Tomatoes** (halved)
1	**Egg** (hard boiled, sliced)
75g	**Smoked Mackerel**

Dressing

¼	**Lemon** (juice only)
1 clove	**Garlic** (minced)
1 tbsp	**Crème Fraîche** (light)
1 tsp	**Horseradish Sauce**

Preparation

1. Layer the **salad leaves** and **asparagus** on a plate, then top with the **tomatoes**, **egg** and **mackerel**.
2. Whisk the **dressing** until well combined and drizzle over the salad.
3. Season with salt & pepper and serve.

5g	27g	28g	7g	2g		1½	375
Carbs	Protein	Fat	SatFat	Fibre		5-a-day	Cals

Nutrition Fact
Mackerel is thought to help prevent the onset of dementia

Leave off dressing to save:
40 Cals 3g Fat

Size
Medium
295g

Cucumber & Fennel

Our lowest calorie salad – get stuck in for only 55 cals!

Ingredients

40g	**Fennel** (sliced)
¼	**Cucumber** (sliced)

Dressing

1 sprig	**Dill** (chopped)
¼	**Lemon** (juice only)
1 tsp	**Olive Oil** (extra virgin)

Preparation

1. Whisk the **dressing** until mixed well.
2. Layer the **fennel** and **cucumber** on a plate and finish with dressing drizzled over.

55 Cals

1½ 5-a-day

2g Fibre

1g SatFat

5g Fat

1g Protein

2g Carbs

Size
Small
140g

Leave off dressing to save:
40 Cals **4g Fat**

Nutrition Fact
Cucumbers contain fisetin, which protects brain health

Sweet Ginger Cabbage

Red cabbage with honey and ginger make this
a sweet treat with very few calories

Ingredients

40g	**Red Cabbage** (leaves)
½	**Red Apple** (sliced)
80g	**Fennel** (sliced)

Dressing

1 tsp	**White Wine Vinegar**
½ inch	**Ginger** (minced)
1 tbsp	**Orange Juice**
1 tsp	**Honey**

Preparation

1. Lay a bed of **red cabbage** leaves on a plate.
2. Whisk the **dressing** until well combined.
3. Mix the **apple** and **fennel** with the dressing and serve on top of the cabbage.

18g	2g	1g	0g	5g		2½	85
Carbs	Protein	Fat	SatFat	Fibre		5-a-day	Cals

Recipe Tip
Add extra ginger if you want
a stronger punchier flavour

Leave off dressing to save:
25 Cals   **6g Carbs**

Size
Small
230g

Bittersweet Grapefruit Treat

Love it bitter? This salad has it covered!

Ingredients

1	handful **Spinach**
20g	**Chicory** leaves
⅓	**Red Grapefruit** (sliced)

Dressing

1 tsp	**Honey**
1 tsp	**Sherry Vinegar**
1 tbsp	**Orange Juice** (fresh)
1 tsp	**Olive Oil** (extra virgin)

Preparation

1. Whisk the **dressing** until well combined.
2. Layer the **spinach**, **chicory** leaves and then **grapefruit** on a plate and finish with a drizzle of dressing.

90 Cals

1½ 5-a-day

2g Fibre

1g SatFat

4g Fat

1g Protein

12g Carbs

Size
Small
150g

Leave off dressing to save:
60 Cals   6g Carbs   4g Fat

Recipe Tip
Pink grapefruit can be used if preferred

Herbed Triple Tomato

If you like tomatoes, why not have them three ways?

Ingredients

4	**Tomatoes** (small, sliced)
¼	**Lime** (juice only)
8	**Cherry Tomatoes** (halved)
30g	**Sun-dried Tomatoes** (chopped)

Dressing

1 sprig	**Tarragon** (chopped)
2 sprigs	**Parsley** (chopped)
6	**Basil** leaves (torn)

Preparation

1. Arrange the **sliced tomatoes** on a plate and squeeze over the **lime juice**.

2. Mix the **cherry tomatoes** and **sun-dried tomatoes** and place on top of the sliced tomatoes.

3. Serve with chopped **herbs** and salt & pepper.

11g Carbs	3g Protein	4g Fat	1g SatFat	5g Fibre		2½ 5-a-day	95 Cals

Recipe Tip

Try to seek out locally-grown tomatoes as they are often tastier and also reduce your carbon footprint!

Size
Medium
285g

Sesame Prawn

Fish sauce, lime and mirin give the prawns a great lift in this simple and elegant salad

Ingredients

1 tsp	**Sesame Seeds**
70g	**King Prawns** (cooked)
40g	**Little Gem Lettuce** (torn)
¼	**Cucumber** (peeled, deseeded, chopped)

Dressing

1 tsp	**Mirin**
½ tsp	**Fish Sauce**
¼	**Lime** (juice only)
1 tsp	**Soy Sauce**

Preparation

1. Whisk the **dressing** together until well combined.
2. Mix the **sesame seeds**, **prawns** and **cucumber** together with the dressing.
3. Serve on a bed of **little gem lettuce** leaves.

105 Cals

1½ 5-a-day

1g Fibre

0g SatFat

3g Fat

14g Protein

5g Carbs

Size
Small
215g

Leave off dressing to save:
20 Cals
4g Carbs

Recipe Tip
Substitute the little gem for cos lettuce for a similar taste

Chilli Prawn & Beansprout

A fiery combination of chilli and prawns

Ingredients

1 clove	**Garlic**	(minced)
¼	**Green Chilli**	(sliced)
¼	**Red Chilli**	(sliced)
70g	**King Prawns**	(raw)
80g	**Beansprouts**	
80g	**Pak Choi**	(root removed)
1	**Carrot**	(ribboned)

Preparation

1. Add the **garlic, chilli, prawns** and 2 tbsp water to a pan over a medium heat.

2. Cook until the prawns turn pink and are fully cooked (about 5 mins).

3. Add **beansprouts** and cook for a further 2 mins.

4. Meanwhile, layer the **pak choi** and **carrot** on a plate.

5. Serve the prawn mixture on top of the layered salad and finish with salt & pepper.

12g Carbs	16g Protein	1g Fat	0g SatFat	6g Fibre	3 5-a-day	115 Cals

Nutrition Fact
Prawns are a great source of good quality protein

Size
Medium
325g

Peach & Parma Ham

Warm, griddled peaches are the star of this tasty dish

Ingredients

1   **Peach** (halved)
1   handful **Rocket**
6   **Mint** leaves (torn)
2   **Parma Ham** slices (torn)

Dressing

1 tsp   **Water**
1 tsp   **Honey**
1 tsp   **Balsamic Vinegar**

Preparation

1. Add the **peach** halves to a hot griddle, flesh side down, until they start to caramelise.
2. Whisk the **dressing** until well combined.
3. Mix the **rocket** and **mint** and place on a plate. Top with the **Parma ham** and peaches.
4. Serve with the dressing drizzled over.

130 Cals

1 5-a-day

3g Fibre

1g SatFat

3g Fat

9g Protein

17g Carbs

Size
Small
200g

Leave off dressing to save:
25 Cals   6g Carbs

Recipe Tip
Choose fragrant peaches with a 'bounce' when pressed

Carrot & Apple Slaw

Coleslaw is so 1970s! Bring your coleslaw up-to-date with this alternative take on a classic

Ingredients
1   **Apple** (small, grated)
1 tbsp   **Raisins** (heaped)
1   **Carrot** (grated)

Dressing
1 tsp   **Red Wine Vinegar**
¼   **Lemon** (juice only)

Preparation

1. Whisk the **dressing** until mixed well and stir through grated **apple**.
2. Top with the grated **carrot** and sprinkle with **raisins**. Season with salt & pepper and serve.

32g Carbs	2g Protein	1g Fat	0g SatFat	5g Fibre	2½ 5-a-day	135 Cals

Nutrition Fact
Carrots are high in vitamin A, which is known to protect your eyes and help with vision

Size
Small
245g

Scallop, Ham & Citrus

Sometimes the simplest salads pack the best flavours
– you can't go wrong with this great dish

Ingredients

6	**Scallops** (small, raw)
1	handful **Rocket**
⅓	**Red Grapefruit**
1	**Parma Ham** slice (torn)

Preparation

1. Dry fry the **scallops** for around 2-3 mins on each side, until just cooked.
2. Arrange the **rocket** on a plate with the **grapefruit** and **Parma ham**.
3. Top with the scallops and serve.

140 Cals

1 5-a-day

2g Fibre

1g SatFat

2g Fat

21g Protein

8g Carbs

Size	Nutrition Fact
Small 210g	Scallops are a source of magnesium, which helps to calm and relax muscles

Honey Mustard Beets

Pack in those antioxidants with this yummy beetroot and feta salad

Ingredients

1	handful **Spinach**	
1	handful **Rocket**	
2	**Beetroot** (small, boiled)	
25g	**Feta** (crumbled)	
1	**Spring Onion** (sliced)	
5	**Mint** leaves	

Dressing

1 tsp	Water
1 tsp	Honey
1 tsp	Balsamic Vinegar
1 tsp	Wholegrain Mustard

Preparation

1. On a plate, layer the **spinach**, **rocket**, **beetroot** and **feta**.

2. Whisk the **dressing** until mixed well and drizzle over the salad.

3. Top with the **spring onion** and **mint** leaves.

15g Carbs	8g Protein	6g Fat	4g SatFat	3g Fibre	1½ 5-a-day	145 Cals

Nutrition Fact
Beetroot has been shown to lower blood pressure

Leave off dressing to save:
35 Cals **7g Carbs**

Size
Small
180g

Crunchy Barbecue Chicken

Go Texan with our take on a southern-style salad

Ingredients

1 tbsp	**Barbecue Sauce**
1/2	**Celery** stalk (sliced)
40g	**Sweetcorn** (tinned)
1/2	**Red Pepper** (sliced)
1/6	**Red Onion** (thinly sliced)
80g	**Chicken Breast** (grilled, sliced)

Preparation

1. Mix together **all the ingredients** except the chicken.
2. Top with the **chicken** and serve.

195 Cals

2 5-a-day

4g Fibre

1g SatFat

3g Fat

28g Protein

16g Carbs

Size
Small
275g

Leave off BBQ sauce to save:
20 Cals   5g Carbs

Recipe Tip
A great way to use up chicken left over from Sunday lunch

Creamy Nut Crunch

If you like a bit of crunch to your salad, this flavoursome combo is for you

Ingredients

½	**Celery** stalk (1cm pieces)
½	**Red Apple** (cubed)
2 tbsp	**Peanuts** (toasted)
20g	**Radishes** (sliced)

Dressing

1 tbsp	**Crème Fraîche** (half fat)
¼	**Lemon** (juice only)
2 sprigs	**Parsley** (chopped)
½ tsp	**Dijon Mustard**

Preparation

1. Whisk the **dressing**.
2. Combine **all the salad ingredients** with the dressing and enjoy.

14g Carbs	7g Protein	12g Fat	3g SatFat	3g Fibre	2 5-a-day	195 Cals

Nutrition Fact

Did you know peanuts actually belong to the legume family?

Leave off dressing to save: **30 Cals** **3g Fat**

Size
Small
195g

Quinoa & Kale

A scrumptious dish of garlic king prawns with a chilli kick

Ingredients

1 tsp	Olive Oil
70g	King Prawns (raw)
1 clove	Garlic
2	handfuls Kale
80g	cooked Quinoa
1 pinch	Chilli Flakes
¼	Lemon (juice only)

Preparation

1. Heat **oil** in pan over medium heat and fry the **prawns** for 2 mins. Add the **garlic** and **kale**, and cook for a further 2 mins or until the prawns are fully cooked.

2. Stir the prawn mixture and **quinoa** together, adding the **chilli flakes** and **lemon juice**.

3. Serve seasoned with salt & pepper.

195 Cals

½ 5-a-day

4g Fibre

1g SatFat

7g Fat

17g Protein

16g Carbs

Size
Small
215g

Nutrition Fact
Kale is rich in lutein, an antioxidant which helps to keep our eyes healthy

Rocky Steak

Peppery rocket and succulent steak – a high protein treat!

Ingredients

1 tsp	**Olive Oil**
100g	**Beef Sirloin** (raw, lean)
4	**Chestnut Mushrooms** (sliced)
1	handful **Rocket**

Dressing

1 tsp	**Olive Oil** (extra virgin)
1 tsp	**Balsamic Vinegar**

Preparation

1. Heat the **oil** in pan on a high heat. Season **steak** with salt & pepper and cook with the **mushrooms** for 4 mins (2 mins each side for steak).
2. Whisk the **balsamic vinegar** and **oil** until well combined.
3. Serve the steak and mushrooms on a bed of **rocket**, and finish with the dressing and any remaining pan juices.

2g Carbs	25g Protein	13g Fat	3g SatFat	1g Fibre

1 5-a-day

225 Cals

Nutrition Fact

The body more easily absorbs iron from steak than from veg

Leave off dressing to save: **45 Cals** **4g Fat**

Size
Medium
195g

Tropical Chicken

Mango and ginger give this chicken a totally tropical taste

Ingredients

½	**Mango** (cubed)
80g	**Pineapple** (cubed)
⅙	**Red Onion** (sliced)
1	large handful **Watercress**
20g	**Little Gem Lettuce** (torn)
80g	**Chicken Breast** (grilled, sliced)

Dressing

1 tsp	Honey
2 tsp	Soy Sauce
½ inch	Ginger (minced)
2 tsp	Rice Wine Vinegar

Preparation

1. Whisk the **dressing** until mixed well.
2. Combine **all the salad ingredients** and stir through the dressing.

240 Cals

2½ 5-a-day

5g Fibre

1g SatFat

2g Fat

28g Protein

28g Carbs

Size
Medium
330g

Leave off dressing to save:
30 Cals   7g Carbs

Recipe Tip
Rocket can be used in place of watercress for a similar flavour

Asian Broccoli

Oriental flavours packed with colour and goodness

Ingredients

½	**Yellow Pepper** (thinly sliced)
1	**Spring Onion** (thinly sliced)
80g	**Broccoli** (cooked)
60g	**Soya Beans** (cooked)
1 tbsp	**Cashews** (toasted)

Dressing

½ inch	**Ginger** (minced)
1 clove	**Garlic** (minced)
1 tsp	**Sesame Oil**
1 tbsp	**Soy Sauce**

Preparation

1. Whisk the **dressing** until well combined.
2. Mix **all the salad vegetables** together and stir through dressing.
3. Serve with the **cashew nuts**.

14g Carbs 14g Protein 13g Fat 2g SatFat 8g Fibre

3 5-a-day 240 Cals

Nutrition Fact
Phytosterols in soya can lower cholesterol

Leave off dressing to save:
50 Cals 3g Carbs 4g Fat

Size
Medium
265g

Squash & Barley

A beautiful looking salad filled with flavour

Ingredients

80g	**Butternut Squash** (cubed)
1 tsp	**Olive Oil**
1/3	**Red Onion** (chunks)
80g	cooked **Pearl Barley**
4	**Olives** (small, halved)
40g	**Broccoli** (cooked)
20g	**Sun-dried Tomato** (chopped)

Dressing

1 tsp	**Chilli Oil**

Preparation

1. Coat the **squash** with the **oil** and roast for 20 mins at 180°C.
2. Add the **onion** and cook for a further 10 mins.
3. When cooked, combine **all the salad ingredients**.
4. Dress with the **chilli oil**, salt & pepper.

270 Cals

2½ 5-a-day

9g Fibre

2g SatFat

13g Fat

6g Protein

35g Carbs

Size
Medium
250g

Leave off dressing to save:
35 Cals 4g Fat

Nutrition Fact
Pearl barley is low in fat and calories but high in fibre

Warm Cauli Bean

A healthy, hearty dish with raisin flavourbombs

Ingredients

1 tsp	**Olive Oil**
2	**Cauliflower** florets (sliced)
2	handfuls **Kale**
80g	**Butter Beans** (tinned)
80g	cooked **Pearl Barley**
2 sprigs	**Parsley** (chopped)
1 tbsp	**Pumpkin Seeds**
1 tbsp	**Raisins** (heaped)

Dressing

¼	**Lemon** (juice only)
½ tsp	**Dijon Mustard**
1 tsp	**Olive Oil** (extra virgin)

Preparation

1. Whisk the **dressing** until well combined.

2. Heat the **oil** in a pan over medium heat and add the **cauliflower**. After 3-4 mins, add the **kale** and cook for a further 1-2 mins.

3. Add the **remaining ingredients** to warm vegetables and drizzle with dressing.

27g Carbs	11g Protein	14g Fat	2g SatFat	9g Fibre

3 5-a-day

275 Cals

Recipe Tip
Roasting cauliflower gives it a deliciously nutty flavour

Leave off dressing to save:
40 Cals 4g Fat

Size
Medium
255g

Chorizo & Rosemary

Get that Spanish feeling with this tasty jumble

Ingredients

50g	**Chorizo** (sliced)
1 sprig	**Rosemary** (chopped)
100g	**New Potatoes** (boiled, cubed)
2 sprigs	**Parsley** (chopped)
2	handfuls **Lambs Lettuce**
80g	**Roasted Red Pepper** (from jar, sliced)

Preparation

1. Dry fry the **chorizo** and **rosemary** until crispy.
2. Mix the chorizo with the **potato**, **pepper** and **parsley**.
3. Serve on a bed of **lettuce**, drizzled with any juices from the pan.

295 Cals

1 5-a-day

4g Fibre

6g SatFat

17g Fat

15g Protein

23g Carbs

Size
Medium
255g

Recipe Tip
Run out of rosemary? Oregano would work just as well

Anchovy Shroom Pasta

If you love anchovies, this pasta salad is sure to hit the spot

Ingredients

40g	**Mushrooms** (sliced)
4	**Cherry Tomatoes**
1 tsp	**Olive Oil**
1	**Spring Onion** (sliced)
1 clove	**Garlic** (minced)
100g	cooked **Fusilli Pasta** (cooled)
3	**Anchovies** (finely chopped)
80g	**Broad Beans** (boiled)
1 sprig	**Rosemary** (chopped)
1	handful **Spinach**
20g	**Little Gem Lettuce** (torn)

Dressing

1 tsp	**Olive Oil** (extra virgin)

Preparation

1. Sauté the **mushrooms** and **tomatoes** in **oil** for 3 mins.
2. Add the **spring onion** & **garlic** to the pan for a further 1 min.
3. When cooked, mix **all the ingredients** together with the remaining **oil** and pepper, and serve on a bed of **spinach** and **lettuce**.

35g Carbs	14g Protein	12g Fat	2g SatFat	12g Fibre	2½ 5-a-day	295 Cals

Recipe Tip
Salty anchovies mean you won't need any extra salt seasoning

Leave off dressing to save: **35 Cals** **4g Fat**

Size
Medium
330g

Cheese & Greens

A nutty combination of green veg and goat's cheese

Ingredients

1 tbsp	**Pine Nuts**
80g	**Green Beans** (boiled)
80g	**Broccoli** (cooked)
25g	**Goat's Cheese** (cubed)
100g	**New Potatoes** (boiled, quartered)

Dressing

¼	**Lemon** (juice only)
2 sprigs	**Dill** (finely chopped)
1 tsp	**Olive Oil** (extra virgin)

Preparation

1. Mix together all the **salad ingredients** except the goat's cheese.
2. Whisk the **dressing** and thoroughly coat the salad.
3. Top with the **goat's cheese** and serve.

300 Cals

2 5-a-day

8g Fibre

6g SatFat

18g Fat

14g Protein

22g Carbs

Size
Medium
315g

Leave off dressing to save:
40 Cals | 4g Fat

Nutrition Fact
Broccoli is high in vitamin K, which helps to heal wounds

Peach, Fig & Blue Cheese

A sweet and salty taste sensation

Ingredients

1	**Peach** (sliced)
1	large handful **Watercress**
2	**Dried Figs** (chopped)
1	handful **Spinach**
25g	**Dolcelatte**
2	**Parma Ham** slices
1 tbsp	**Walnuts** (chopped)

Dressing

½ tsp	**Dijon Mustard**
¼	**Lemon** (juice only)
1 tbsp	**Crème Fraîche** (half fat)

Preparation

1. Roast the **peach** at 180°C for 10 mins.
2. Meanwhile, combine all the **remaining salad ingredients** except the ham and walnuts.
3. Whisk the **dressing** and mingle with the salad.
4. Top with the **Parma ham**, roasted peach and **walnuts**.

28g Carbs	16g Protein	16g Fat	8g SatFat	7g Fibre		2½ 5-a-day	310 Cals

Recipe Tip
When in season, use 2 fresh figs (instead of dried) to save 40 cals

Leave off dressing to save: 30 Cals | 3g Fat

Size
Medium
300g

Pesto Chickpeas

Pesto and cheese? Yes please!

Ingredients
25g	**Feta** (cubed)
1	handful **Spinach**
80g	**Chickpeas** (tinned)
⅙	**Red Onion** (thinly sliced)
1 tbsp	**Pine Nuts** (toasted)

Dressing
1 tsp	**Water**
1 tbsp	**Basil Pesto**

Preparation

1. Mix **all the salad ingredients** except the pine nuts.
2. Combine the **dressing** and toss through the salad.
3. Sprinkle the **pine nuts** over the top and enjoy!

310 Cals

1½ 5-a-day

6g Fibre

5g SatFat

21g Fat

13g Protein

16g Carbs

Size
Small
170g

Leave off dressing to save:
65 Cals **6g Fat**

Nutrition Fact
80g chickpeas count as one of your 5-a-day. Easy peasy!

Strawberry Rocket

Try this unusual mix of strawberries and halloumi – we think you're going to love it!

Ingredients

2   handfuls **Rocket**
4   **Strawberries** (thinly sliced)
50g   **Halloumi** (sliced, dry fried)
1 tbsp **Pecans** (chopped)

Dressing

2 tsp   **Olive Oil** (extra virgin)
1 tsp   **Balsamic Vinegar**
1 tsp   **Honey**

Preparation

1. Layer the salad, starting with **rocket** on the bottom, followed by **strawberries** then **halloumi**.
2. Sprinkle with the **pecans**.
3. Whisk the **dressing** and drizzle over the salad.

13g Carbs	15g Protein	27g Fat	10g SatFat	4g Fibre

1½ 5-a-day   **355** Cals

Nutrition Fact
Pecans contain the antioxidant phenolic

Leave off dressing to save:
95 Cals | 6g Carbs | 8g Fat

Size
Small 200g

Walnut, Ham & Stilton

Powerful flavours to energise your taste buds

Ingredients

1	large handful **Watercress**
1	handful **Lambs Lettuce**
½	**Red Apple** (sliced)
2	**Parma Ham** slices (torn)
1 tbsp	**Walnuts** (chopped)
25g	**Stilton** (crumbled)

Dressing

2 tsp	**Red Wine Vinegar**
2 tsp	**Olive Oil** (extra virgin)
1 tsp	**Wholegrain Mustard**

Preparation

1. Mix together the **watercress, lambs lettuce** and **apple**.
2. Whisk the **dressing** and combine with the salad.
3. Top with the **Parma ham, walnuts** and **stilton**.

355 Cals

1½ 5-a-day

2g Fibre

9g SatFat

28g Fat

16g Protein

25g Carbs

Size
Medium
200g

Leave off dressing to save:
80 Cals | 15g Carbs | 9g Fat

Recipe Tip
Replace walnuts with pecans if preferred

Leafy Cheesy Pasta

Pack in some greens with this scrumptious pasta salad

Ingredients

80g	**Tender Stem Broccoli** (blanched)
20g	**Sun-dried Tomatoes** (chopped)
100g	cooked **Pasta Bows** (cooled)
40g	**Chicory** leaves (torn)
1	handful **Spinach**

Dressing

1 tbsp	**White Wine Vinegar**
1 tsp	**Olive Oil** (extra virgin)
¼	**Lemon** (juice only)
25g	**Dolcelatte**

Preparation

1. Mix **all the salad ingredients**.
2. Blend the **dressing** until smooth and stir through the salad, seasoning with pepper.

38g Carbs	14g Protein	17g Fat	7g SatFat	9g Fibre	2 5-a-day	355 Cals

Recipe Tip
Swap dolcelatte for gorgonzola, which has similar nutrition values

Leave off dressing to save: **140 Cals** **13g Fat**

Size
Medium
315g

Puy Lentil & Anchovy

A great looking salad that is high in fibre
and contains 3 of your 5-a-day

Ingredients

80g	**Broccoli**
½	**Lemon** (peel only, grated)
2 tsp	**Olive Oil**
2 sprigs	**Parsley** (chopped)
⅙	**Red Onion** (sliced)
120g	cooked **Puy Lentils**
8	**Cherry Tomatoes** (halved)

Dressing

1 tsp	**Red Wine Vinegar**
1 tsp	**Olive Oil** (extra virgin)
3	**Anchovies** (chopped)

Preparation

1. Mix the **broccoli** and **lemon peel** with the **oil** and roast at 180°C for 10 mins.
2. Whisk together the **dressing**, mashing in the **anchovies**.
3. Combine **all the ingredients** with the dressing and serve.

360 Cals

3 5-a-day

13g Fibre

2g SatFat

16g Fat

19g Protein

31g Carbs

Size
Medium
320g

Leave off dressing to save:
60 Cals   5g Fat

Recipe Tip
Short on time? Use pre-cooked lentils instead of dried ones

Apricot Quinoa

A lovely vegetarian salad with nuts and quinoa

Ingredients

3	**Dried Apricots** (chopped)
1/3	**Courgette** (matchsticks)
10	**Mint** leaves (chopped)
1	handful **Watercress**
1/4	**Avocado** (chopped)
1 tbsp	**Raisins** (heaped)
80g	cooked **Quinoa**
1 tbsp	**Almonds** (toasted)

Dressing

1 tsp	**Tahini**
1 clove	**Garlic** (minced)
1/4	**Lemon** (juice only)
25g	**Greek Yogurt** (fat free)

Preparation

1. Mix **all the salad ingredients** except the almonds.
2. Whisk together the **dressing**.
3. Spoon the dressing on top of the salad and sprinkle with **almonds**.

37g	13g	18g	3g	9g
Carbs	Protein	Fat	SatFat	Fibre

3	360
5-a-day	Cals

Nutrition Fact
Quinoa is the perfect grain choice if you are on a gluten-free diet

Leave off dressing to save:
50 Cals 3g Fat

Size
Medium
305g

Mean Green Pumpkin

Wonderful creamy textures in every bite

Ingredients

25g	**Feta** (cubed)
20g	**Alfalfa Sprouts**
1	handful **Spinach**
½	**Avocado** (cubed)
1 tbsp	**Pumpkin Seeds**
8	**Olives** (small, chopped)
80g	**Asparagus Tips** (blanched)

Dressing

1 tsp	**Honey**
½ tsp	**Dijon Mustard**
¼	**Lime** (juice only)
1 tsp	**Olive Oil** (extra virgin)

Preparation

1. Muddle together **all the salad ingredients**.
2. Whisk the **dressing** and toss through the salad.

365 Cals

2½ 5-a-day

8g Fibre

8g SatFat

31g Fat

12g Protein

10g Carbs

Size
Medium
275g

Leave off dressing to save:
60 Cals   5g Carbs   4g Fat

Recipe Tip
Omit the pumpkin seeds to save 55 cals

Wild Fruity Rice

A wild, tropical experience for your palate

Ingredients

1	**Spring Onion** (thinly sliced)
100g	cooked **Wild Rice**
1/3	**Orange** (cubed)
1/2	**Mango** (cubed)
2 tbsp	**Cashews**

Dressing

1 tsp	**Olive Oil** (extra virgin)
1/4	**Lime** (juice only)
1 tbsp	**Orange Juice**
1 tsp	**Fish Sauce**

Preparation

1. Mix **all the salad ingredients**.
2. Whisk together the **dressing** and mix through the salad.

55g Carbs   **11g** Protein   **15g** Fat   **3g** SatFat   **7g** Fibre   **2** 5-a-day   **380** Cals

Nutrition Fact
Wild rice contains more antioxidants than brown rice

Leave off dressing to save:
45 Cals **4g Fat**

Size
Medium
320g

Sugar Snap Salmon

Pearl barley and sugar snap peas complement the salmon to make an appetising dish

Ingredients

100g	**Salmon** (raw, small fillet)
40g	**Sugar Snap Peas**
80g	cooked **Pearl Barley**
1/6	**Courgette** (matchsticks)
40g	**Asparagus Tips** (blanched)

Dressing

1/2	**Red Chilli**
5	**Mint** leaves
1 sprig	**Dill** (chopped)
1/4	**Lemon** (juice only)
1 tsp	**Olive Oil** (extra virgin)
1 tsp	**Wholegrain Mustard**

Preparation

1. Season the **salmon** with salt & pepper and cook in the oven at 180°C for 12-15 mins.
2. Whisk the **dressing** until well combined.
3. Flake the salmon and gently **mix everything together**.

390 Cals

1½ 5-a-day

6g Fibre

3g SatFat

18g Fat

33g Protein

26g Carbs

Size
Medium
310g

Leave off dressing to save:
45 Cals **5g Fat**

Nutrition Fact
Eating your sugar snaps peas raw retains all their vitamins

Pecan, Kale & Cranberry

Packed full of healthy nutrients to boost your day

Ingredients

2	handfuls **Kale**
1 tbsp	**Dried Cranberries** (heaped)
3	**Dried Apricots** (chopped)
2 sprigs	**Parsley** (chopped)
1 tbsp	**Pecans** (chopped)
100g	cooked **Wild Rice**
1/3	**Orange** (cubed)

Dressing

1/2 tsp	**Honey**
1/2 tsp	**Dijon Mustard**
1 tsp	**Red Wine Vinegar**
1 tsp	**Olive Oil** (extra virgin)
2 tsp	**Orange Juice** (fresh)

Preparation

1. Bake the **kale** at 180°C for 5 mins (no oil).
2. Whisk the **dressing**.
3. Combine **all the salad ingredients** with the warm kale and dressing.

63g Carbs **9g** Protein **13g** Fat **1g** SatFat **8g** Fibre

2½ 5-a-day **395** Cals

Nutrition Fact
Zinc-rich Pecans are good for healing

Leave off dressing to save:
60 Cals **5g Carbs** **4g Fat**

Size
Medium
305g

Ciabatta Eggspress

Basil, ciabatta and egg make a wonderful Italian salad

Ingredients

50g	**Ciabatta** (toasted)
1 clove	**Garlic**
8	**Cherry Tomatoes** (halved)
1/6	**Red Onion** (thinly sliced)
1	handful **Lambs Lettuce**
12	**Basil** leaves
1	**Egg** (hard boiled, halved)
1 tbsp	**Pine Nuts** (toasted)

Dressing

1/4	**Lemon** (juice only)
2 tsp	**Olive Oil** (extra virgin)
1 tbsp	**White Wine Vinegar**

Preparation

1. Rub the **ciabatta** with **garlic**, then cut into cubes.
2. Jumble together the ciabatta, **tomatoes**, **onion**, **lettuce** and **basil**.
3. Make the **dressing** and pour over the salad.
4. Place the **egg** on top and sprinkle with **pine nuts**.

400 Cals

1½ 5-a-day

4g Fibre

4g SatFat

23g Fat

17g Protein

32g Carbs

Size
Medium
285g

Leave off dressing to save:
75 Cals   8g Fat

Recipe Tip
You could try lemon basil in this dish for a citrus twist

Roasted Cauli & Chickpeas

Crunchy chickpeas and roasted cauliflower
with a lemony avocado zing

Ingredients

4	**Cauliflower** florets (chopped)
80g	**Chickpeas** (tinned)
1 tsp	**Olive Oil**
1	large handful **Lambs Lettuce**
50g	**Goat's Cheese**

Dressing

¼	**Lemon** (juice only)
1 clove	**Garlic**
¼	**Avocado**

Preparation

1. Toss the **cauliflower** and **chickpeas** in the **oil** and bake at 180°C for 20 mins.
2. When cooked, muddle together the warm salad with the **lambs lettuce** and top with the **goat's cheese**.
3. Whizz the **dressing** in a blender until smooth and spoon over the salad.

22g Carbs	22g Protein	27g Fat	11g SatFat	9g Fibre

2½ 5-a-day

410 Cals

Nutrition Fact
If you love garlic, doubling the quantity only adds 5 extra cals!

Leave off dressing to save: **70 Cals** **7g Fat**

Size
Small
340g

Sweet Potato & Rosemary

A cacophony of textures to please and delight

Ingredients

80g	**Sweet Potato** (cubed)
1 tsp	**Olive Oil**
2	handfuls **Rocket**
80g	cooked **Wild Rice**
1 tbsp	**Cashews** (chopped)
20g	**Sun-dried Tomatoes** (chopped)

Dressing

1 tsp	**Honey**
1 clove	**Garlic**
¼	**Lemon** (juice only)
2 tsp	**Olive Oil** (extra virgin)
1 sprig	**Rosemary** leaves (finely chopped)

Preparation

1. Bake the **sweet potato** with 1 tsp **oil** for 20-30 mins at 180°C.
2. Meanwhile, whisk the **dressing**.
3. Jumble **all the ingredients** with the dressing and serve.

415 Cals

2 5-a-day

8g Fibre

3g SatFat

20g Fat

10g Protein

51g Carbs

Size
Medium
245g

Leave off dressing to save:
90 Cals **5g Carbs** **8g Fat**

Recipe Tip
Add any other fresh herbs of your liking

Creamy Prawn Orzo

Packed with 34g protein, this will fill you up for hours

Ingredients

4	**Cherry Tomatoes** (quartered)
40g	**Broccoli** (blanched, chopped)
40g	**Asparagus Tips** (blanched)
100g	**King Prawns** (cooked)
100g	cooked **Orzo Pasta**
40g	**Soya Beans**

Dressing

¼	**Avocado**
1 clove	**Garlic**
1	**Spring Onion**
¼	**Lime** (juice only)
2 sprigs	**Coriander** (large)
50g	**Greek Yogurt** (fat free)

Preparation

1. Combine **all the salad ingredients**.
2. Blend together the **dressing**, mingle with the salad and season with salt & pepper.

42g Carbs	34g Protein	11g Fat	2g SatFat	8g Fibre

2½ 5-a-day

415 Cals

Recipe Tip
Use wholemeal pasta to boost the fibre

Leave off dressing to save:
100 Cals **4g Carbs** **7g Fat**

Size
Medium
470g

Berry Pecan Cheese

Our raspberry balsamic dressing is a winner every time

Ingredients

25g	**Stilton** (cubed)	
1	handful **Spinach**	
1 tbsp	**Pecans** (chopped)	
½	**Avocado** (chopped)	
4	**Strawberries** (quartered)	
20g	**Little Gem Lettuce** (torn)	

Dressing

1 tsp	**Honey**
8	**Raspberries**
1 tbsp	**Balsamic Vinegar**
1 tsp	**Olive Oil** (extra virgin)

Preparation

1. Mix **all the salad ingredients**.
2. Blitz the **dressing** in a blender until smooth.
3. Pour the dressing over the salad.

425 Cals

3 5-a-day

9g Fibre

10g SatFat

34g Fat

10g Protein

19g Carbs

Size
Medium
290g

Leave off dressing to save:
90 Cals 12g Carbs 4g Fat

Recipe Tip
Avocados ripen more slowly in the fridge

Mango Tango Noodles

A delicious, Asian-inspired noodle salad

Ingredients

70g	cooked **Egg Noodles** (cooled)
2 sprigs	**Coriander** (chopped)
80g	**Pak Choi** (chopped)
¼	**Red Pepper** (sliced)
1 tbsp	**Peanuts** (chopped)
½	**Mango** (cubed)

Dressing

1 inch	**Ginger** (minced)
¼	**Lime** (juice only)
2 tsp	**Sesame Oil**

Preparation

1. Mix **all the salad ingredients**.
2. Stir the **dressing** together and toss through salad.

67g Carbs	13g Protein	14g Fat	2g SatFat	9g Fibre	2½ 5-a-day	435 Cals

Recipe Tip
Add more lime juice if you want a zingier citrus punch!

Leave off dressing to save: **75 Cals** **8g Fat**

Size
Medium
305g

Chorizo, Egg & Bean

Sun-dried tomato dressing is the perfect partner to chorizo and egg

Ingredients

50g	**Chorizo** (sliced)
100g	**New Potatoes** (boiled, cubed)
80g	**Green Beans** (blanched)
2 sprigs	**Parsley** (chopped)
1	**Egg** (hard boiled, quartered)

Dressing

40g	**Sun-dried Tomatoes**
1 tbsp	**White Wine Vinegar**

Preparation

1. Whisk together the **dressing**.
2. Dry fry the **chorizo** until crispy. When cooked, stir in the **potatoes** and dressing.
3. Serve on a plate surrounded with the **green beans**.
4. Add the **parsley** and **egg**, drizzling over any juices from the pan.

445 Cals

1½ 5-a-day

8g Fibre

8g SatFat

27g Fat

26g Protein

23g Carbs

Size
Medium
345g

Leave off dressing to save:
75 Cals   **3g Carbs**   **5g Fat**

Nutrition Fact
Eggs are a source of vitamin B2

Cranberry Couscous

A fruity, nutty salad to put a smile on your face

Ingredients

1	**Stock Cube**
160ml	**Water** (boiled)
70g	**Couscous** (dry)
1	handful **Mixed Salad Leaves**
1 tbsp	**Dried Cranberries** (heaped)
1/2	**Red Apple** (sliced, quartered)
1 sprig	**Rosemary** leaves (chopped)
8	**Olives** (small, chopped)
2 sprigs	**Parsley** (chopped)
1 sprig	**Thyme** (chopped)
1 tbsp	**Walnuts** (chopped)
1/4	**Lemon** (juice only)

Preparation

1. Dissolve the **stock cube** in boiling water.
2. Add the stock to the **couscous** and cover for 5 mins.
3. Mingle together **all the ingredients** and serve.

79g Carbs	11g Protein	12g Fat	2g SatFat	7g Fibre		2 5-a-day	455 Cals

Nutrition Fact
Apples contain soluble fibre, known to slow down digestion and be beneficial for heart health

Size
Medium
405g

Cumin Roasted Chickpeas

Get 5 of your 5-a-day for just 235 cals!

Ingredients

80g	**Chickpeas** (tinned)
1 tsp	**Cumin Seeds**
1/2	**Onion** (sliced)
1 tsp	**Olive Oil**
1/2	**Carrot** (ribboned)
1/2	**Celery** stalk (sliced)
1/2	**Apple** (thinly sliced)
1/3	**Courgette** (ribboned)
6	**Basil** leaves

Preparation

1. Roast the **chickpeas**, **cumin seeds**, **onion** and **oil** at 180°C for 20 mins, shaking occasionally.

2. When cooked, combine **all the ingredients**, top with **basil** and serve.

235 Cals

5 5-a-day

10g Fibre

1g SatFat

8g Fat

9g Protein

34g Carbs

Size
Large
380g

Nutrition Fact
If you like carrots then double up the quantity to bulk out your plate, only adding an extra 15 cals!

Roasted Winter Warmer

Perfect for a cold winter's day

Ingredients

80g	**Butternut Squash** (peeled, cubed)
1	**Raw Beetroot** (peeled, cubed)
1/3	**Red Onion** (wedges)
1/2	**Red Pepper** (sliced)
80g	**Aubergine** (cubed)
1/3	**Courgette** (cubed)
2 cloves	**Garlic** (skin on)
1 tbsp	**Olive Oil**
1 tsp	**Sumac**

Dressing

1 sprig	**Parsley** (large)
1/4	**Lemon** (juice only)
50g	**Greek Yogurt** (fat free)

Preparation

1. Combine **all the salad ingredients** with the **oil** and **sumac**. Roast in the oven at 190°C for 30 mins.
2. Assemble the warm salad on a plate, squeezing the garlic cloves out of their skins.
3. Stir together the **dressing** and drizzle over the salad.

27g Carbs	10g Protein	14g Fat	2g SatFat	12g Fibre		5½ 5-a-day	270 Cals

Recipe Tip

If you don't have sumac, try another herb such as rosemary

Leave off dressing to save: **30 Cals** **3g Carbs**

Size
Small
370g

Butter Bean & Fennel

All 5 of your 5-a-day with just 5 ingredients
– simple, healthy and delicious

Ingredients

200g **Butter Beans** (tinned)
80g **Fennel** (finely sliced)
80g **Olives** (quartered)
4 handfuls **Watercress**
8 **Cherry Tomatoes** (halved)

Preparation

1. Mix the **butter beans**, **fennel**, and **olives**.
2. Arrange the **watercress** and **tomatoes** on top, seasoning with salt & pepper.

280 Cals	5 5-a-day	21g Fibre	2g SatFat	11g Fat	17g Protein	31g Carbs

Size
Large
520g

Recipe Tip
If butter beans don't tantalise your tastebuds, use cannellini beans, or any other beans of your choice

Beans & Goat's Cheese

A large plate of yumminess with all your
5-a-day and only 12g carbs!

Ingredients

80g	**Green Beans** (blanched, halved)
8	**Cherry Tomatoes** (halved)
25g	**Goat's Cheese** (cubed)
8	**Olives** (small, chopped)
80g	**Soya Beans** (cooked)
¼	**Cucumber** (cubed)
40g	**Radishes** (sliced)

Dressing

1 tbsp	**Capers**
¼	**Lemon** (juice only)
2 sprigs	**Rosemary** (chopped)
2 tsp	**Olive Oil** (extra virgin)

Preparation

1. Thoroughly mix all the **salad ingredients**.
2. Whisk the **dressing** and drizzle over the salad.

12g Carbs	19g Protein	24g Fat	7g SatFat	10g Fibre		5 5-a-day	350 Cals

Recipe Tip
Green olives tend to have a sharper taste than black olives

Leave off dressing to save: 80 Cals 8g Fat

Size
Large
445g

Blueberry Flame

Set alight your appetite with this vibrant wonder

Ingredients

1	**Carrot** (ribbons)
½	**Red Apple** (sliced)
¼	**Red Onion** (sliced)
1 tbsp	**Hazelnuts** (chopped)
80g	**Red Cabbage** (sliced)
2 tbsp	**Dried Cranberries**

Dressing

1 tsp	**Honey**
40g	**Blueberries**
½ tsp	**Dijon Mustard**
2 tsp	**Balsamic Vinegar**
2 tsp	**Olive Oil** (extra virgin)

Preparation

1. Muddle together the **salad ingredients**.
2. Using a blender, whizz up the **dressing** and drizzle over the salad.

385 Cals

5 5-a-day

10g Fibre

2g SatFat

16g Fat

4g Protein

57g Carbs

Size
Medium
375g

Leave off dressing to save:
125 Cals 11g Carbs 8g Fat

Nutrition Fact
Blueberries give an antioxidant boost

Roast Veg Satay

Peanut and lime is simply sublime with roasted veggies

Ingredients

80g	**Butternut Squash** (cubed)
2 tsp	**Olive Oil**
4	**Cauliflower** florets
1/3	**Red Onion** (sliced)
2 cloves	**Garlic** (skin on)
1	**Carrot** (cubed)
2	handfuls **Kale**
80g	**Soya Beans** (cooked)
1 sprig	**Coriander** (large)
1 tbsp	**Cashews**

Dressing

1 tbsp	**Satay Sauce**
1/4	**Lime** (juice only)

Preparation

1. Combine the **squash** with half the **oil**. Roast in the oven for 10 mins at 180°C.
2. Add the **cauliflower, onion, garlic, carrots** and remaining oil and cook for 15 mins more.
3. Add the **kale** and roast for a further 5 mins.
4. Combine the veg with the **other salad ingredients**.
5. Whisk the **dressing** and pour over the salad.

29g Carbs	18g Protein	21g Fat	3g SatFat	13g Fibre

5 5-a-day

385 Cals

Nutrition Fact
Vegetables and nuts offer lots of fibre

Leave off dressing to save:
30 Cals 3g Carbs 2g Fat

Size
Medium
380g

Thai Vegan

Ingredients

100g	**Tofu** (firm, cubed)
1 tsp	**Sesame Oil**
40g	**Beansprouts**
20g	**Radishes** (sliced)
1	**Carrot** (matchsticks)
2 sprigs	**Coriander** (chopped)
40g	**Red Cabbage** (sliced)
2	**Spring Onions** (sliced)
1/3	**Courgette** (matchsticks)
1/4	**Cucumber** (matchsticks)
1/4	**Yellow Pepper** (matchsticks)

Dressing

1 tbsp	**Soy Sauce**
1/4	**Lime** (juice only)
1 clove	**Garlic** (minced)
1/2 inch	**Ginger** (minced)
2 tbsp	**Peanut Butter**
1 tbsp	**Rice Wine Vinegar**

Preparation

1. Dry **tofu** between paper towels. Rub with **oil** and bake for 45 mins at 180°C, until crispy.
2. Mix **all the other salad ingredients**.
3. Whisk the **dressing** and stir through the salad, topping with the tofu.

390 Cals	**5** 5-a-day		**10g** Fibre	**4g** SatFat	**23g** Fat	**20g** Protein	**25g** Carbs

Size
Large
560g

Leave off dressing to save:
200 Cals | 8g Carbs | 15g Fat

Recipe Tip
Use peanut butter without added salt

Sweet & Sour Rice

Ingredients

2	handfuls **Mixed Salad Leaves**
40g	**Sugar Snap Peas** (blanched)
8	**Cherry Tomatoes** (halved)
40g	**Asparagus tips** (blanched)
80g	**Green Beans** (blanched)
2	**Spring Onions** (halved)
80g	**Broccoli** (blanched)
100g	cooked **Wild Rice**
20g	**Radishes** (sliced)
1 tbsp	**Cashews**

Dressing

1 tsp	**Honey**
2 tsp	**Sesame Oil**
1 inch	**Ginger** (peeled)
¼	**Lemon** (juice only)
1 tsp	**Balsamic Vinegar**
1 tsp	**Rice Wine Vinegar**
3 sprigs	**Coriander** (chopped)

Preparation

1. Jumble together the **salad ingredients** (except the cashews).
2. Whisk together the **dressing** and toss through the salad.
3. Top with **cashew nuts** and serve.

53g Carbs	17g Protein	15g Fat	3g SatFat	13g Fibre

5 5-a-day   **405** Cals

Nutrition Fact
This salad has nearly half your daily fibre!

Leave off dressing to save:
100 Cals | 7g Carbs | 8g Fat

Size
Large 560g

Pear & Pomegranate

An assortment of colours and wholesome goodness

Ingredients

½	**Pear** (sliced)
50g	**Feta** (crumbled)
1 tbsp	**Sultanas** (heaped)
½	**Red Apple** (sliced)
⅛	**Cucumber** (sliced)
1	handful **Salad Leaves**
⅓	**Red Onion** (thinly sliced)
½	**Red Pepper** (thinly sliced)
2 tbsp	**Pomegranate Seeds** (heaped)

Dressing

2 tsp	**Balsamic Vinegar**
2 tsp	**Olive Oil** (extra virgin)

Preparation

1. Mix **all the salad ingredients** except the pomegranate seeds.
2. Whisk the **dressing**, drizzle over the salad and top with **pomegranate seeds**.

405 Cals

5 5-a-day

8g Fibre

8g SatFat

19g Fat

11g Protein

47g Carbs

Size
Medium
465g

Leave off dressing to save:

90 Cals **4g Carbs** **8g Fat**

Nutrition Fact
Pomegranates are rich in antioxidants

Rainbow Tahini

Elegantly balanced with a tasty tahini dressing, this salad contains 6 of your 5-a-day!

Ingredients

1	**Spring Onion**	(thinly sliced)
8	**Cherry Tomatoes**	(halved)
½	**Yellow Pepper**	(sliced)
80g	**Butter Beans**	(tinned)
40g	**Broccoli**	(chopped)
1 tbsp	**Sunflower Seeds**	
5	**Mint** leaves	(torn)
½	**Avocado**	(cubed)
20g	**Alfalfa Sprouts**	
2	handfuls **Salad Leaves**	

Dressing

1 tbsp	**Tahini**	
½	**Lemon**	(juice only)

Preparation

1. Mix together **all the ingredients** except the salad leaves.
2. Arrange the **salad leaves** on a plate and top with the mixture.
3. Stir together the **dressing** and drizzle over the salad.

25g Carbs	18g Protein	29g Fat	5g SatFat	18g Fibre		6 5-a-day	430 Cals

Recipe Tip
Omit the sunflower seeds to keep this dish under 400 cals

Leave off dressing to save: **100 Cals** **9g Fat**

Size
Large
500g

Fiery Fiesta

The taste of a Mexican fiesta on your plate

Ingredients

2	handfuls **Rocket**
½	**Avocado** (cubed)
40g	**Sugar Snap Peas**
40g	**Sweetcorn** (tinned)
½	**Red Pepper** (sliced)
80g	**Black Beans** (tinned)

Dressing

2 drops	**Tabasco**
¼	**Lime** (juice only)
2 sprigs	**Coriander**
½	**Red Chilli** (finely chopped)

Preparation

1. Whisk the **dressing** until well combined.
2. Mix the **salad ingredients**, stir through dressing and serve.

260 Cals

4½ 5-a-day

13g Fibre

3g SatFat

15g Fat

10g Protein

18g Carbs

Size
Medium
365g

Recipe Tip
If you like it extra hot, add more Tabasco to this spicy dish!

Broad Bean & Feta

An effortless ensemble that packs in 10g fibre

Ingredients

80g **Butter Beans** (tinned)
40g **Broad Beans** (boiled)
40g **Peas** (boiled)
25g **Feta** (crumbled)

Dressing

1 large handful **Watercress**
2 tsp **Olive Oil** (extra virgin)
5 **Mint** leaves (chopped)
½ **Lemon** (peel only, grated)

Preparation

1. Jumble **all the salad ingredients** together except the feta.
2. Stir together the **dressing** and mix through the salad.
3. Top with the **feta**, and salt & pepper.

17g Carbs	14g Protein	15g Fat	5g SatFat	10g Fibre

2 5-a-day

260 Cals

Recipe Tip
Spinach would work well instead of watercress

Leave off dressing to save:
75 Cals 8g Fat

Size
Small
215g

Asparagus Goat's Cheese

The minty dressing is perfect with creamy goat's cheese and new potatoes

Ingredients

100g	**New Potatoes** (boiled, chopped)
80g	**Asparagus Tips** (blanched)
80g	**Broad Beans** (cooked)
1	handful **Spinach**
25g	**Goat's Cheese** (crumbled)

Dressing

1 tsp	**Olive Oil** (extra virgin)
5	**Mint** leaves (chopped)
1 tsp	**Balsamic Vinegar**
1	**Spring Onion** (finely chopped)

Preparation

1. Mix together the **potatoes**, **asparagus** and **beans**.
2. Make the **dressing** and stir through the salad.
3. Serve on a bed of **spinach**, topped with the **goat's cheese**.

260 Cals

2½ 5-a-day

10g Fibre **5g** SatFat **12g** Fat **14g** Protein **25g** Carbs

Size
Medium
325g

Leave off dressing to save:
45 Cals 4g Fat

Recipe Tip
Blanch using a small amount of water to minimise vitamin loss

Roasted Vegetable Delight

Caramelised heaven on a plate

Ingredients

1/3	**Red Onion** (roughly chopped)
80g	**Butternut Squash** (sliced)
1/2	**Red Pepper** (small, sliced)
80g	**Chickpeas** (tinned)
80g	**Aubergine** (sliced)
1 tsp	**Olive Oil**
8	**Cherry Tomatoes**

Dressing

1 tsp	**Honey**
1 tsp	**Balsamic Vinegar**
1 tsp	**Olive Oil** (extra virgin)

Preparation

1. Mix together the **onion, squash, pepper, chickpeas** and **aubergine** with 1 tsp **oil**. Bake for 20 mins at 180°C.
2. Stir the vegetables, add the **tomatoes** and cook for a further 10 mins.
3. Whisk the **dressing** until well combined, stir through the warm vegetables and serve.

37g Carbs	9g Protein	11g Fat	2g SatFat	12g Fibre	5½ 5-a-day	280 Cals

Recipe Tip
Use a whole onion for an extra 30 cals

Leave off dressing to save:
60 Cals 6g Carbs 4g Fat

Size
Medium 325g

Chickpea & Apricot

An unconventional mingle of dried apricots, chickpeas, carrots and chicory

Ingredients

1	**Carrot**	(grated)
1 clove	**Garlic**	(minced)
80g	**Chickpeas**	(tinned)
2 sprigs	**Coriander**	(chopped)
6	**Dried Apricots**	(chopped)
20g	**Chicory**	(leaves)
1 tbsp	**Pumpkin Seeds**	

Dressing

1 tsp	**Red Wine Vinegar**	
2 tsp	**Olive Oil**	(extra virgin)

Preparation

1. Whisk the **dressing** until well combined.

2. Mix **all the salad ingredients** together except the chicory and pumpkin seeds.

3. Serve on a bed of **chicory** leaves and finish with the **pumpkin seeds**.

310 Cals

3 5-a-day

12g Fibre

2g SatFat

16g Fat

10g Protein

35g Carbs

Size
Small
240g

Leave off dressing to save:
75 Cals   8g Fat

Nutrition Fact
Apricots are a great non-dairy source of calcium

Warm Squash & Houmous

Smoky houmous is a great addition to this kale and squash salad

Ingredients

80g	**Butternut Squash** (cubed)
½	**Yellow Pepper** (sliced)
1 tsp	**Olive Oil**
2	handfuls **Kale**
1 tbsp	**Pumpkin Seeds**

Dressing

2 tbsp	**Water**
2 tsp	**Tahini**
1 clove	**Garlic** (minced)
½ tsp	**Cumin** (ground)
½ tsp	**Smoked Paprika**
¼	**Lemon** (juice only)
80g	**Chickpeas** (tinned)

Preparation

1. Bake the **squash** and **pepper** at 180°C with 1 tsp **oil** for 20 mins.
2. Add the **kale** and cook for 5 mins more.
3. Meanwhile, blitz the **dressing** in a blender to make the houmous.
4. Serve the salad topped with the houmous & **pumpkin seeds**.

28g Carbs   **14g** Protein   **18g** Fat   **3g** SatFat   **12g** Fibre

3½ 5-a-day   **320** Cals

Recipe Tip
Swap pine nuts for pumpkin seeds

Leave off dressing to save:
170 Cals   15g Carbs   9g Fat

Size
Medium
315g

Three Bean & Tomato

Packed with a massive 19g fibre, this three bean vegan salad also has a low GI

Ingredients

1 clove	**Garlic** (minced)
1/6	**Red Onion** (sliced)
2	handfuls **Salad Leaves**
80g	**Kidney Beans** (tinned)
80g	**Black Eye Beans** (tinned)
80g	**Cannellini Beans** (tinned)

Dressing

10	**Basil** leaves
40g	**Sun-dried Tomatoes**
1 tbsp	**White Wine Vinegar**

Preparation

1. Whizz the **dressing** together in a blender, adding water if too thick.
2. Combine **all the salad ingredients**.
3. Stir the dressing through the bean mixture and serve.

330 Cals

4½ 5-a-day

19g Fibre

1g SatFat

6g Fat

20g Protein

45g Carbs

Size
Medium
370g

Leave off dressing to save:

75 Cals **4g Carbs** **5g Fat**

Nutrition Fact
Beans have a low GI, helping you feel full

Halloumi & Orange

It really does taste as good as it looks

Ingredients

160g	**Butternut Squash**	(cooked, cubed)
80g	**Chickpeas**	(tinned)
1 tsp	**Olive Oil**	
50g	**Halloumi**	(sliced)
⅓	**Orange**	(peeled, chopped)
40g	**Alfalfa Sprouts**	
1	handful **Rocket**	

Dressing

¼	**Lemon**	(juice only)
1 tbsp	**Orange Juice**	(fresh)
1 tsp	**Olive Oil**	(extra virgin)

Preparation

1. Mix the **squash** and **chickpeas** with the **oil**, salt & pepper and bake at 180°C for 25 mins.
2. Dry fry the **halloumi** in a hot pan for 1-2 mins each side.
3. Combine the cooked veg with the **remaining salad ingredients**.
4. Whisk the **dressing** until mixed well. Stir through the salad and top with halloumi.

35g Carbs	23g Protein	23g Fat	10g SatFat	10g Fibre		4 5-a-day	425 Cals

Recipe Tip

Omit the cheese for a nutritious vegan salad (and save 155 cals)

Leave off dressing to save: **40 Cals** **4g Fat**

Size
Medium
400g

Roasted Roots & Lentils

A curious combination of roasted roots with a strawberry dressing

Ingredients

1	**Raw Beetroot**	(peeled, cubed)
80g	**Butternut Squash** (peeled, cubed)	
1	**Parsnip** (quartered)	
1 clove	**Garlic** (minced)	
2 tsp	**Olive Oil**	
2	handfuls **Watercress**	
120g	cooked **Puy Lentils**	
25g	**Goat's Cheese** (cubed)	

Dressing

2	**Strawberries**	
½ tsp	**Dijon Mustard**	
¼	**Lemon** (juice only)	
2 tsp	**Balsamic Vinegar**	
1 tsp	**Red Wine Vinegar**	

Preparation

1. Roast the **beetroot, squash, parsnip** and **garlic** in **oil** for 30 mins at 180°C.
2. Whisk the **dressing** well.
3. Add the **watercress** to the cooked veg, stir in the **lentils** and dressing, and top with the **goat's cheese**.

480 Cals

5 5-a-day

17g Fibre
6g SatFat
19g Fat
23g Protein
53g Carbs

Size
Medium
440g

Leave off dressing to save:
40 Cals **7g Carbs**

Nutrition Fact
Parsnips are a great source of soluble and insoluble fibre

Tahini, Squash & Nuts

Go nuts for this wonderful mix

Ingredients

160g	**Butternut Squash** (cubed)
1 tsp	**Olive Oil**
1 tbsp	**Pomegranate Seeds** (heaped)
40g	**Little Gem Lettuce** (torn)
1 sprig	**Thyme** (leaves, chopped)
80g	**Soya Beans** (cooked)
1 tbsp	**Cashews** (chopped)
1 tbsp	**Walnuts** (chopped)
¼	**Red Apple** (sliced)
1 tbsp	**Pumpkin Seeds**

Dressing

1 clove	**Garlic**
1 tsp	**Tahini**
¼	**Lemon** (juice only)
25g	**Greek Yogurt** (fat free)

Preparation

1. Roast the **squash** in the **oil** at 180°C for 20-30 mins.
2. When cooked, mix the squash with the **remaining salad ingredients**.
3. Whisk the **dressing** and spoon over the salad.

32g Carbs	22g Protein	29g Fat	4g SatFat	11g Fibre		3½ 5-a-day	485 Cals

Nutrition Fact
Nuts are a source of vitamin E, known to keep skin healthy

Leave off dressing to save: 50 Cals 3g Fat

Size
Medium
385g

Mango Chicken & Salsa

Mango and lime combined is a totally delicious combo!

Ingredients

150g	**Chicken Breast** (raw)
2	handfuls **Spinach**
¼	**Green Pepper** (sliced)
¼	**Red Pepper** (sliced)

Dressing

½	**Mango** (cubed)
½	**Lime** (juice only)
2 sprigs	**Parsley** (finely chopped)
1	**Red Chilli** (finely chopped)

Preparation

1. Season the **chicken** breast with salt & pepper and cook in the oven for 15-20 mins at 180°C or until fully cooked.

2. Meanwhile, mix the **dressing** in a bowl to make the salsa.

3. To serve, arrange the **spinach** and **peppers** on a plate, add the sliced chicken and dress with the mango salsa.

235 Cals

2½ 5-a-day

6g Fibre

1g SatFat

2g Fat

39g Protein

16g Carbs

Size
Medium
315g

Nutrition Fact
Mango is a source of vitamin A, which boosts your immune system and assists vision in low light

Tuna & Bean

Packed with 26g protein for only 265 calories

Ingredients

40g	**Asparagus Tips** (blanched)
80g	**Cannellini Beans** (tinned)
1/3	**Red Onion** (thinly sliced)
2	handfuls **Spinach**
70g	**Tuna** (tinned)

Dressing

2 tsp	**Olive Oil** (extra virgin)
1 tbsp	**White Wine Vinegar**
1/2 clove	**Garlic** (crushed)
1 sprig	**Parsley** (large)
1 sprig	**Dill**

Preparation

1. Mix **all the salad ingredients** and season with salt & pepper.
2. Whisk the **dressing** until well combined and gently stir through the salad.

17g Carbs	26g Protein	10g Fat	2g SatFat	8g Fibre	2½ 5-a-day	265 Cals

Recipe Tip
Use any fresh herbs of your choice in this dressing

Leave off dressing to save:
80 Cals   8g Fat

Size
Medium
300g

Crab, Avo & Asparagus

A light, refreshing and summery salad

Ingredients

100g	**Crab** (tinned)
1/4	**Mango** (cubed)
1/4	**Avocado** (cubed)
1	handful **Salad Leaves**
8	**Cherry Tomatoes** (halved)
80g	**Asparagus Tips** (blanched)

Dressing

2 sprigs	**Parsley** (chopped)
1/4	**Lemon** (juice only)
2 tsp	**Olive Oil** (extra virgin)
1/2	**Lemon** (peel only, grated)

Preparation

1. Combine **all the salad ingredients**.
2. Stir together the **dressing** and toss through the salad.

280 Cals

3½ 5-a-day

7g Fibre

3g SatFat

16g Fat

23g Protein

12g Carbs

Size
Medium
385g

Leave off dressing to save:
75 Cals   8g Fat

Nutrition Fact
Crab is low in calories and contains high quality protein

Mustard Chicken

This chicken and wholegrain mustard fusion is a great way to fill up with 33g protein in one dish

Ingredients

80g	**Chicken Breast** (grilled, sliced)
2	handfuls **Mixed Salad Leaves**
4	**Cherry Tomatoes** (quartered)
80g	**Black Eye Beans** (tinned)
1 sprig	**Tarragon** (chopped)

Dressing

1 tsp	**Wholegrain Mustard**
1 tsp	**White Wine Vinegar**
2 tsp	**Olive Oil** (extra virgin)

Preparation

1. Whisk the **dressing** together until mixed well.
2. Combine the **salad ingredients** and gently stir through dressing.
3. Season with salt & pepper and serve.

16g Carbs	33g Protein	11g Fat	2g SatFat	5g Fibre	2 5-a-day	305 Cals

Recipe Tip
Use any salad leaves you like in this mustardy dish

Leave off dressing to save: **80 Cals** **9g Fat**

Size
Medium
260g

Smoked Mackerel & Ginger

Simple, quick, tasty and packed with omega-3

Ingredients

1	handful **Spinach**
1/3	**Courgette** (ribboned)
80g	**Butter Beans** (tinned)
75g	**Smoked Mackerel**

Dressing

1/2 inch	**Ginger**
2 tsp	**Soy Sauce**
1/4	**Lime** (juice only)

Preparation

1. Whisk the **dressing** until mixed well.
2. Mix **all the salad ingredients** except the mackerel and gently stir through the dressing.
3. Slice the **mackerel** and serve on top of the salad.

315 Cals

2½ 5-a-day

6g Fibre

4g SatFat

19g Fat

23g Protein

14g Carbs

Size
Medium
280g

Nutrition Fact
Mackerel contains omega-3 fatty acids, which helps to lower your risk of heart disease

Chicken Waldorf

Our high protein version of this classic dish

Ingredients

80g	**Chicken Breast** (grilled, torn)
1	large handful **Watercress**
8	**Green Grapes** (halved)
½	**Celery** stalk (chopped)
¼	**Red Apple** (chopped)
1 tbsp	**Walnuts** (chopped)

Dressing

½ tsp	**Dijon Mustard**
1 sprig	**Tarragon** (chopped)
3 tbsp	**Crème Fraîche** (half fat)

Preparation

1. Mix **all the salad ingredients**.
2. Whisk the **dressing** until well combined and stir through the salad.
3. Season with salt & pepper and serve.

14g Carbs	30g Protein	16g Fat	6g SatFat	2g Fibre	1½ 5-a-day	315 Cals

Nutrition Fact
Walnuts are anti-inflammatory, so ideal for those with arthritis

Leave off dressing to save: **75 Cals** **7g Fat**

Size
Medium
280g

Dill Salmon & Potato

Who said potato salad should be boring?
This one is sure to delight

Ingredients

100g	**Salmon** (raw, small fillet)
1	**Spring Onion** (sliced)
100g	**New Potatoes** (boiled, cubed)
1	large handful **Lambs Lettuce**
1	**Raw Beetroot** (peeled, grated)

Dressing

1 sprig	**Dill** (chopped)
¼	**Lemon** (juice only)
50g	**Greek Yogurt** (fat free)

Preparation

1. Season the **salmon** with salt & pepper and bake at 180°C for 12-15 mins or until cooked.
2. Flake the salmon and combine with the **spring onion** and **potatoes**, gently mixing in the **dressing ingredients**.
3. Layer the **lambs lettuce** and **beetroot** on a plate, and add the salmon mixture on top.

345 Cals

1½ 5-a-day

4g Fibre

3g SatFat

13g Fat

34g Protein

26g Carbs

Size
Medium
360g

Leave off dressing to save:
30 Cals **3g Carbs**

Recipe Tip
Pre-cooked beetroot can be used if raw beetroot is not available

Greens, Egg & Ham

Wonderful, peppery watercress compliments the egg and Parma ham in this simple-to-prepare salad

Ingredients

80g	**Green Beans** (blanched, halved)
100g	**New Potatoes** (boiled, cubed)
1	large handful **Watercress**
2	**Eggs** (hard boiled, halved)
2	**Parma Ham** slices (grilled)

Dressing

1 tsp	**White Wine Vinegar**
1 tsp	**Olive Oil** (extra virgin)
½ tsp	**Dijon Mustard**
1 tbsp	**Water**

Preparation

1. Mix together the **green beans**, **potatoes** & **watercress**.
2. Grill the **Parma ham** for 1-2 mins until slightly crispy.
3. Arrange the salad on a plate and top with the **eggs** and torn ham.
4. Whisk the **dressing** until mixed well and pour over the salad.

19g Carbs	28g Protein	20g Fat	5g SatFat	5g Fibre		1 5-a-day	360 Cals

Nutrition Fact
Frozen green beans are just as nutritious as fresh ones

Leave off dressing to save:
40 Cals   4g Fat

Size
Medium 370g

Sticky Citrus Salmon

At a whopping 37g, this is our highest protein salad – so much goodness on one elegant plate!

Ingredients

150g	**Salmon** (raw, large fillet)
1	large handful **Watercress**
2	boiled **Beetroot** (sliced)
1/6	**Orange** (sliced)
1 tsp	**Sesame Seeds**

Dressing

1 tsp	**Soy Sauce**
1 tsp	**Sesame Oil**
1 clove	**Garlic** (minced)
1/2 inch	**Ginger** (minced)
1/4	**Lemon** (juice only)

Preparation

1. Place the **salmon** on a piece of foil, whisk the **dressing** and pour over the salmon. Fold the foil tightly to allow fish to steam. Bake at 180°C for 15-18 mins or until cooked.

2. On a plate, layer the **watercress**, **beetroot** and **orange** slices.

3. Place the sticky salmon fillet on top, pour over any juices from the foil and sprinkle with the **sesame seeds**.

385 Cals

2 5-a-day

3g Fibre

4g SatFat

21g Fat

37g Protein

13g Carbs

Size
Medium
310g

Leave off dressing to save:
45 Cals   4g Fat

Nutrition Fact
Salmon is a source of omega-3, which boosts brain health

Quinoa, Egg & Broccoli

A nutritious marriage of high protein ingredients

Ingredients

4	**Cherry Tomatoes** (quartered)
1	**Spring Onion** (finely sliced)
40g	**Broccoli** (cooked, chopped)
40g	**Sugar Snap Peas** (halved)
80g	cooked **Quinoa**
1	**Egg** (hard boiled, quartered)
1 tbsp	**Pumpkin Seeds** (toasted)

Dressing

1 tbsp	**Water**
1 tbsp	**Tahini**
¼	**Lemon** (juice only)
1 clove	**Garlic** (finely chopped)
2 sprigs	**Parsley** (finely chopped)

Preparation

1. Mix **all the salad ingredients** except the egg and pumpkin seeds.
2. Whisk the **dressing** until well combined and stir through salad.
3. Serve topped with the **egg** and scattered with **pumpkin seeds**.

25g Carbs	24g Protein	22g Fat	4g SatFat	9g Fibre	2 5-a-day	390 Cals

Nutrition Fact
Eggs are an excellent source of high quality protein

Leave off dressing to save: 105 Cals 9g Fat

Size
Medium
370g

Mexican Flame

5 Cals

2 sprigs	**Coriander** (chopped)
1/4	**Lime** (juice only)
1/2	**Red Chilli** (chopped)
2 drops	**Tabasco**

0g Carbs
0g Fat

Tasty Thai

25 Cals

1 tsp	**Fish Sauce**
1/4	**Lime** (juice only)
1 tsp	**Mirin**
1 tsp	**Soy Sauce**

4g Carbs
0g Fat

Creamy Parsley Tang

30 Cals

1 tbsp	**Crème Fraîche**
1/2 tsp	**Dijon Mustard**
1/4	**Lemon** (juice only)
2 sprigs	**Parsley** (chopped)

1g Carbs
3g Fat

Lemon Dill

40 Cals

1 sprig	**Dill** (chopped)
1/4	**Lemon** (juice only)
1 tsp	**Olive Oil** (extra virgin)

0g Carbs
4g Fat

Strawberry Balsamic *(blended)*

40 Cals

2 tsp	**Balsamic Vinegar**
1/2 tsp	**Dijon Mustard**
1 clove	**Garlic**
1/4	**Lemon** (juice only)
1 tsp	**Red Wine Vinegar**
2	**Strawberries**

7g Carbs
1g Fat

Creamy Horseradish

2g Carbs
3g Fat

40 Cals

1 tbsp	Crème Fraîche (half fat)
1 clove	Garlic (minced)
1 tsp	Horseradish Sauce
¼	Lemon (juice only)

Chilli Mint Mix-up

1g Carbs
5g Fat

45 Cals

1 sprig	Dill (chopped)
¼	Lemon (juice only)
5	Mint leaves (chopped)
1 tsp	Olive Oil (extra virgin)
½	Red Chilli (chopped)
1 tsp	Wholegrain Mustard

Moroccan Medley

3g Carbs
3g Fat

55 Cals

1 clove	Garlic (minced)
2 tbsp	Greek Yogurt (fat free)
¼	Lemon (juice only)
1 tsp	Tahini

Sweet & Spicy

5g Carbs
4g Fat

60 Cals

½ tsp	Dijon Mustard
½ tsp	Honey
1 tsp	Olive Oil (extra virgin)
2 tbsp	Orange Juice (fresh)
1 tsp	Red Wine Vinegar

Deep Sea Delight (blended)

0g Carbs
5g Fat

60 Cals

3	Anchovies (finely chopped)
1 tsp	Olive Oil (extra virgin)
1 tsp	Red Wine Vinegar

Herby Tomato (blended)

75 Cals

2 sprigs	Parsley
40g	Sun-dried Tomatoes
1 tbsp	White Wine Vinegar

3g Carbs
5g Fat

Tarragon Cream

80 Cals

3 tbsp	Crème Fraîche (half fat)
½ tsp	Dijon Mustard
2 sprigs	Tarragon (chopped)

2g Carbs
7g Fat

Raspberry Blush (blended)

90 Cals

1 tbsp	Balsamic Vinegar
1 tsp	Honey
1 tsp	Olive Oil (extra virgin)
8	Raspberries

12g Carbs
4g Fat

Yogurt Guacamole (blended)

100 Cals

¼	Avocado
1	small handful Coriander
1 clove	Garlic
50g	Greek Yogurt (fat free)
¼	Lime (juice only)
1	Spring Onion

4g Carbs
7g Fat

Sweet Ginger

100 Cals

1 tsp	Balsamic Vinegar
2 sprigs	Coriander (chopped)
1 inch	Ginger (minced)
1 tsp	Honey
¼	Lemon (juice only)
1 tsp	Rice Wine Vinegar
2 tsp	Sesame Oil

7g Carbs
8g Fat

Classic Balsamic

6g Carbs

8g Fat

100 Cals

1 tsp	Balsamic Vinegar
1 tsp	Honey
2 tsp	Olive Oil (extra virgin)

Blueberry Blast *(blended)*

11g Carbs

8g Fat

125 Cals

2 tsp	Balsamic Vinegar
40g	Blueberries
½ tsp	Dijon Mustard
1 tsp	Honey
2 tsp	Olive Oil (extra virgin)

Rosemay & Garlic

5g Carbs

12g Fat

130 Cals

1 clove	Garlic (minced)
1 tsp	Honey
¼	Lemon (juice only)
1 tbsp	Olive Oil (extra virgin)
1 sprig	Rosemary leaves (chopped)

Blue Cheese *(blended)*

0g Carbs

13g Fat

140 Cals

25g	Dolcelatte
⅛	Lemon (juice only)
1 tsp	Olive Oil (extra virgin)
1 tbsp	White Wine Vinegar

Soy Satay

8g Carbs

19g Fat

240 Cals

1 clove	Garlic (minced)
½ inch	Ginger (minced)
¼	Lime (juice only)
2 tbsp	Peanut Butter (crunchy)
1 tbsp	Rice Wine Vinegar
1 tsp	Sesame Oil
1 tbsp	Soy Sauce

1g Protein
0g Fat
1g Fibre

Asparagus Tips
40g

1g Carbs
10 Cals
½ 5-a-day

2g Protein
0g Fat
2g Fibre

Asparagus Tips
80g

2g Carbs
20 Cals
1 5-a-day

1g Protein
0g Fat
0g Fibre

Alfalfa Sprouts
20g

0g Carbs
5 Cals
0 5-a-day

2g Protein
0g Fat
1g Fibre

Alfalfa Sprouts
40g

0g Carbs
10 Cals
½ 5-a-day

1g Protein
0g Fat
1g Fibre

Artichokes (tinned)
40g, drained

2g Carbs
11 Cals
½ 5-a-day

1g Protein
0g Fat
1g Fibre

Artichokes (tinned)
80g, drained

4g Carbs
23 Cals
1 5-a-day

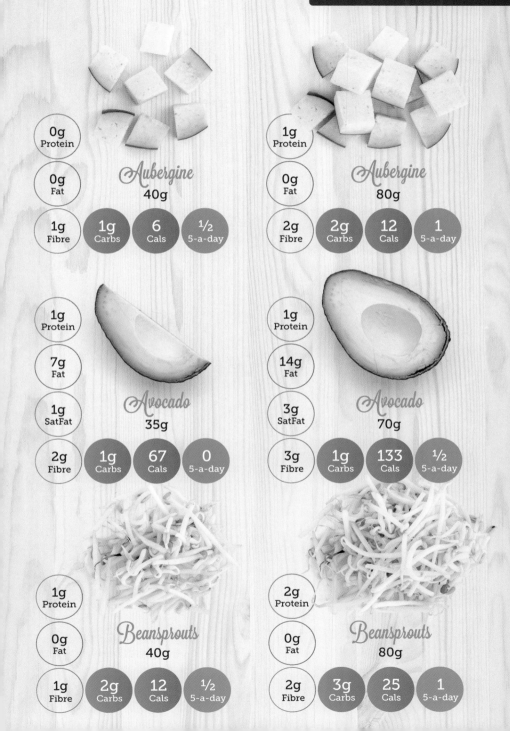

Aubergine
40g

| 0g Protein | 0g Fat | 1g Fibre | 1g Carbs | 6 Cals | ½ 5-a-day |

Aubergine
80g

| 1g Protein | 0g Fat | 2g Fibre | 2g Carbs | 12 Cals | 1 5-a-day |

Avocado
35g

| 1g Protein | 7g Fat | 1g SatFat | 2g Fibre | 1g Carbs | 67 Cals | 0 5-a-day |

Avocado
70g

| 1g Protein | 14g Fat | 3g SatFat | 3g Fibre | 1g Carbs | 133 Cals | ½ 5-a-day |

Beansprouts
40g

| 1g Protein | 0g Fat | 1g Fibre | 2g Carbs | 12 Cals | ½ 5-a-day |

Beansprouts
80g

| 2g Protein | 0g Fat | 2g Fibre | 3g Carbs | 25 Cals | 1 5-a-day |

1g
Protein

0g
Fat

1g
Fibre

Beetroot
40g, ½ medium, peeled

3g
Carbs

14
Cals

½
5-a-day

1g
Protein

0g
Fat

2g
Fibre

Beetroot
80g, peeled

6g
Carbs

29
Cals

1
5-a-day

1g
Protein

0g
Fat

1g
Fibre

Beetroot
40g, small, boiled

4g
Carbs

18
Cals

½
5-a-day

2g
Protein

0g
Fat

2g
Fibre

Beetroot
80g, 2 small, boiled

8g
Carbs

37
Cals

1
5-a-day

3g
Protein

0g
Fat

2g
Fibre

Black Eye Beans (tinned)
40g, drained

7g
Carbs

46
Cals

½
5-a-day

6g
Protein

0g
Fat

4g
Fibre

Black Eye Beans (tinned)
80g, drained

14g
Carbs

91
Cals

1
5-a-day

Broad Beans
40g, boiled

2g Protein
0g Fat
3g Fibre
2g Carbs
19 Cals
½ 5-a-day

Broad Beans
80g, boiled

4g Protein
1g Fat
6g Fibre
4g Carbs
38 Cals
1 5-a-day

Broccoli
40g

2g Protein
0g Fat
2g Fibre
1g Carbs
14 Cals
½ 5-a-day

Broccoli
80g

3g Protein
0g Fat
3g Fibre
3g Carbs
27 Cals
1 5-a-day

Butter Beans (tinned)
40g, drained

2g Protein
0g Fat
2g Fibre
5g Carbs
31 Cals
½ 5-a-day

Butter Beans (tinned)
80g, drained

5g Protein
0g Fat
5g Fibre
10g Carbs
62 Cals
1 5-a-day

Butternut Squash
40g

0g Protein
0g Fat
1g Fibre
3g Carbs
14 Cals
½ 5-a-day

Butternut Squash
80g

1g Protein
0g Fat
2g Fibre
7g Carbs
29 Cals
1 5-a-day

Cabbage
20g

0g Protein
0g Fat
1g Fibre
1g Carbs
5 Cals
0 5-a-day

Cabbage
40g

1g Protein
0g Fat
2g Fibre
2g Carbs
11 Cals
½ 5-a-day

Cabbage, Red
20g

0g Protein
0g Fat
1g Fibre
1g Carbs
4 Cals
0 5-a-day

Cabbage, Red
40g

0g Protein
0g Fat
1g Fibre
1g Carbs
8 Cals
½ 5-a-day

Cannellini Beans (tinned)
40g, drained

3g Protein
0g Fat
2g Fibre
6g Carbs
38 Cals
½ 5-a-day

Cannellini Beans (tinned)
80g, drained

6g Protein
0g Fat
5g Fibre
12g Carbs
75 Cals
1 5-a-day

Capers
10g, 1 tbsp

0g Protein
0g Fat
0g Fibre
0g Carbs
3 Cals
0 5-a-day

Capers
20g, 2 tbsp

0g Protein
0g Fat
1g Fibre
1g Carbs
6 Cals
0 5-a-day

Carrot
40g, ½ medium

0g Protein
0g Fat
2g Fibre
3g Carbs
14 Cals
½ 5-a-day

Carrot
80g, 1 medium

0g Protein
0g Fat
3g Fibre
6g Carbs
27 Cals
1 5-a-day

3g Protein

Chickpeas (tinned)
40g, drained

1g Fat

2g Fibre | 6g Carbs | 46 Cals | ½ 5-a-day

6g Protein

Chickpeas (tinned)
80g, drained

2g Fat

4g Fibre | 13g Carbs | 92 Cals | 1 5-a-day

1g Protein

Cauliflower
40g

0g Fat

1g Fibre | 2g Carbs | 12 Cals | ½ 5-a-day

2g Protein

Cauliflower
80g

0g Fat

1g Fibre | 4g Carbs | 24 Cals | 1 5-a-day

0g Protein

Celery
40g

0g Fat

1g Fibre | 0g Carbs | 3 Cals | ½ 5-a-day

0g Protein

Celery
80g

0g Fat

1g Fibre | 1g Carbs | 6 Cals | 1 5-a-day

Chicory
20g

| 0g Protein | 0g Fat | 0g Fibre | 1g Carbs | 2 Cals | 0 5-a-day |

Chicory
40g

| 0g Protein | 0g Fat | 0g Fibre | 1g Carbs | 4 Cals | ½ 5-a-day |

Chilli
5g

| 0g Protein | 0g Fat | 0g Fibre | 0g Carbs | 1 Cals | 0 5-a-day |

Chilli
10g

| 0g Protein | 0g Fat | 0g Fibre | 0g Carbs | 3 Cals | 0 5-a-day |

Courgette
40g, ⅙ medium

| 1g Protein | 0g Fat | 0g Fibre | 1g Carbs | 7 Cals | ½ 5-a-day |

Courgette
80g, ⅓ medium

| 1g Protein | 0g Fat | 1g Fibre | 1g Carbs | 14 Cals | 1 5-a-day |

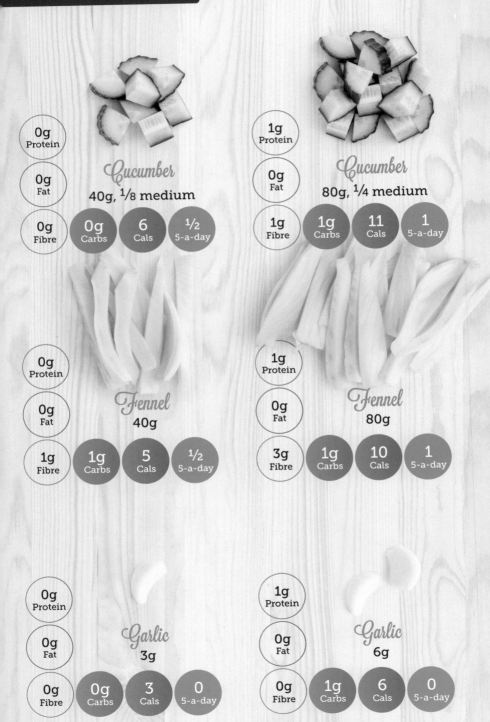

Cucumber

40g, 1/8 medium

0g Protein

0g Fat

0g Fibre

0g Carbs

6 Cals

1/2 5-a-day

Cucumber

80g, 1/4 medium

1g Protein

0g Fat

1g Fibre

1g Carbs

11 Cals

1 5-a-day

Fennel

40g

0g Protein

0g Fat

1g Fibre

1g Carbs

5 Cals

1/2 5-a-day

Fennel

80g

1g Protein

0g Fat

3g Fibre

1g Carbs

10 Cals

1 5-a-day

Garlic

3g

0g Protein

0g Fat

0g Fibre

0g Carbs

3 Cals

0 5-a-day

Garlic

6g

1g Protein

0g Fat

0g Fibre

1g Carbs

6 Cals

0 5-a-day

Gherkins
40g

0g Protein
0g Fat
1g Fibre
1g Carbs
6 Cals
0 5-a-day

Gherkins
80g

1g Protein
0g Fat
1g Fibre
2g Carbs
11 Cals
0 5-a-day

Ginger
5g, 1 inch, peeled

0g Protein
0g Fat
0g Fibre
0g Carbs
2 Cals
0 5-a-day

Ginger
10g, 2 inches, peeled

0g Protein
0g Fat
0g Fibre
1g Carbs
4 Cals
0 5-a-day

Green Beans
40g

1g Protein
0g Fat
1g Fibre
1g Carbs
10 Cals
½ 5-a-day

Green Beans
80g

2g Protein
0g Fat
3g Fibre
2g Carbs
19 Cals
1 5-a-day

Kale
20g, handful

| 1g Protein | 0g Fat | 1g Fibre | 0g Carbs | 7 Cals | 0 5-a-day |

Kale
40g, 2 handfuls

| 1g Protein | 1g Fat | 2g Fibre | 1g Carbs | 13 Cals | ½ 5-a-day |

Kidney Beans (tinned)
40g, drained

| 3g Protein | 0g Fat | 3g Fibre | 6g Carbs | 37 Cals | ½ 5-a-day |

Kidney Beans (tinned)
80g, drained

| 6g Protein | 0g Fat | 7g Fibre | 13g Carbs | 74 Cals | 1 5-a-day |

Leek
40g

| 1g Protein | 0g Fat | 1g Fibre | 1g Carbs | 9 Cals | ½ 5-a-day |

Leek
80g

| 1g Protein | 0g Fat | 2g Fibre | 2g Carbs | 18 Cals | 1 5-a-day |

Lettuce, Lambs
20g, large handful

0g Protein
0g Fat
0g Fibre
0g Carbs
3 Cals
0 5-a-day

Lettuce, Lambs
40g, 2 large handfuls

1g Protein
0g Fat
0g Fibre
1g Carbs
6 Cals
½ 5-a-day

Lettuce
20g

0g Protein
0g Fat
0g Fibre
0g Carbs
2 Cals
0 5-a-day

Lettuce
40g

0g Protein
0g Fat
1g Fibre
1g Carbs
4 Cals
½ 5-a-day

Lentils (tinned)
40g, drained

3g Protein
0g Fat
1g Fibre
7g Carbs
41 Cals
½ 5-a-day

Lentils (tinned)
80g, drained

7g Protein
0g Fat
3g Fibre
14g Carbs
82 Cals
1 5-a-day

Little Gem Lettuce
20g

- **0g** Protein
- **0g** Fat
- **0g** Fibre
- **0g** Carbs
- **2** Cals
- **0** 5-a-day

Little Gem Lettuce
40g

- **0g** Protein
- **0g** Fat
- **1g** Fibre
- **1g** Carbs
- **4** Cals
- **½** 5-a-day

Mangetout
40g

- **1g** Protein
- **0g** Fat
- **1g** Fibre
- **2g** Carbs
- **13** Cals
- **½** 5-a-day

Mangetout
80g

- **3g** Protein
- **0g** Fat
- **2g** Fibre
- **3g** Carbs
- **26** Cals
- **1** 5-a-day

Mixed Beans (tinned)
40g, drained

- **3g** Protein
- **0g** Fat
- **2g** Fibre
- **5g** Carbs
- **39** Cals
- **½** 5-a-day

Mixed Beans (tinned)
80g, drained

- **5g** Protein
- **1g** Fat
- **5g** Fibre
- **10g** Carbs
- **78** Cals
- **1** 5-a-day

0g Protein

0g Fat

Mixed Salad Leaves
20g

0g Fibre   **0g** Carbs   **2** Cals   **0** 5-a-day

0g Protein

0g Fat

Mixed Salad Leaves
40g

1g Fibre   **1g** Carbs   **4** Cals   **½** 5-a-day

0g Protein

0g Fat

Mushrooms
40g

0g Fibre   **0g** Carbs   **3** Cals   **½** 5-a-day

1g Protein

0g Fat

Mushrooms
80g

1g Fibre   **0g** Carbs   **6** Cals   **1** 5-a-day

2g Protein

0g Fat

New Potatoes
100g, boiled

2g Fibre   **15g** Carbs   **68** Cals   **0** 5-a-day

4g Protein

0g Fat

New Potatoes
200g, boiled

4g Fibre   **30g** Carbs   **136** Cals   **0** 5-a-day

1g Protein
0g Fat
2g Fibre

Okra
40g

1g Carbs
12 Cals
½ 5-a-day

2g Protein
1g Fat
4g Fibre

Okra
80g

2g Carbs
25 Cals
1 5-a-day

0g Protein
1g Fat
0g Fibre

Olives (pitted in brine)
12g, drained

0g Carbs
12 Cals
0 5-a-day

0g Protein
3g Fat
1g Fibre

Olives (pitted in brine)
30g, drained

0g Carbs
31 Cals
0 5-a-day

0g Protein
0g Fat
0g Fibre

Onion, Red
20g, ⅙ medium

2g Carbs
7 Cals
0 5-a-day

0g Protein
0g Fat
1g Fibre

Onion, Red
40g, ⅓ medium

3g Carbs
14 Cals
½ 5-a-day

Onion, White
20g, ⅛ medium

- 0g Protein
- 0g Fat
- 0g Fibre
- 2g Carbs
- 7 Cals
- 0 5-a-day

Onion, White
40g, ¼ medium

- 0g Protein
- 0g Fat
- 1g Fibre
- 3g Carbs
- 14 Cals
- ½ 5-a-day

Parsnip
40g

- 1g Protein
- 0g Fat
- 2g Fibre
- 5g Carbs
- 26 Cals
- ½ 5-a-day

Parsnip
80g

- 1g Protein
- 1g Fat
- 4g Fibre
- 10g Carbs
- 51 Cals
- 1 5-a-day

Peas
40g

- 3g Protein
- 1g Fat
- 2g Fibre
- 4g Carbs
- 32 Cals
- ½ 5-a-day

Peas
80g

- 5g Protein
- 1g Fat
- 4g Fibre
- 8g Carbs
- 63 Cals
- 1 5-a-day

1g Protein			
0g Fat	**Pak Choi** 40g		
0g Fibre	1g Carbs	5 Cals	½ 5-a-day

1g Protein			
0g Fat	**Pak Choi** 80g		
1g Fibre	2g Carbs	10 Cals	1 5-a-day

0g Protein			
0g Fat	**Pepper** 40g, ¼ small		
1g Fibre	2g Carbs	9 Cals	½ 5-a-day

1g Protein			
0g Fat	**Pepper** 80g, ½ small		
2g Fibre	4g Carbs	18 Cals	1 5-a-day

0g Protein			
0g Fat	**Radicchio** 20g		
0g Fibre	0g Carbs	3 Cals	0 5-a-day

1g Protein			
0g Fat	**Radicchio** 40g		
1g Fibre	1g Carbs	6 Cals	½ 5-a-day

1g Protein
0g Fat
0g Fibre

Rocket
20g, handful

0g Carbs | 4 Cals | 0 5-a-day

1g Protein
0g Fat
1g Fibre

Rocket
40g, 2 handfuls

0g Carbs | 7 Cals | ½ 5-a-day

0g Protein
0g Fat
0g Fibre

Radishes
40g

1g Carbs | 5 Cals | ½ 5-a-day

1g Protein
0g Fat
1g Fibre

Radishes
80g

2g Carbs | 10 Cals | 1 5-a-day

6g Protein
3g Fat
0g SatFat
3g Fibre

Soya Beans
40g

2g Carbs | 56 Cals | ½ 5-a-day

11g Protein
6g Fat
1g SatFat
6g Fibre

Soya Beans
80g

4g Carbs | 113 Cals | 1 5-a-day

1g Protein

0g Fat

Spinach
20g, handful

1g Fibre

0g Carbs

5 Cals

0 5-a-day

1g Protein

0g Fat

Spinach
40g, 2 handfuls

1g Fibre

1g Carbs

10 Cals

½ 5-a-day

0g Protein

0g Fat

Spring Onion
20g

0g Fibre

1g Carbs

5 Cals

0 5-a-day

1g Protein

0g Fat

Spring Onion
40g

1g Fibre

1g Carbs

9 Cals

½ 5-a-day

1g Protein

0g Fat

Sugar Snap Peas
40g

1g Fibre

2g Carbs

14 Cals

½ 5-a-day

3g Protein

0g Fat

Sugar Snap Peas
80g

2g Fibre

4g Carbs

27 Cals

1 5-a-day

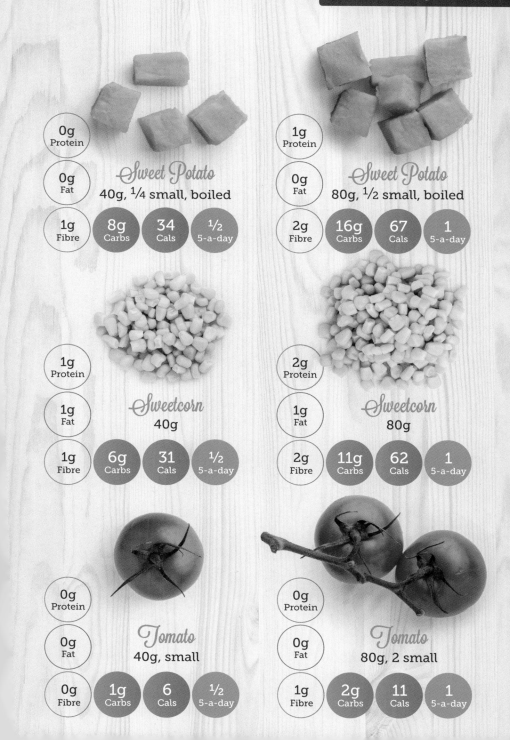

0g Protein

0g Fat

1g Fibre

Sweet Potato
40g, ¼ small, boiled

8g Carbs | **34** Cals | **½** 5-a-day

1g Protein

0g Fat

2g Fibre

Sweet Potato
80g, ½ small, boiled

16g Carbs | **67** Cals | **1** 5-a-day

1g Protein

1g Fat

1g Fibre

Sweetcorn
40g

6g Carbs | **31** Cals | **½** 5-a-day

2g Protein

1g Fat

2g Fibre

Sweetcorn
80g

11g Carbs | **62** Cals | **1** 5-a-day

0g Protein

0g Fat

0g Fibre

Tomato
40g, small

1g Carbs | **6** Cals | **½** 5-a-day

0g Protein

0g Fat

1g Fibre

Tomato
80g, 2 small

2g Carbs | **11** Cals | **1** 5-a-day

0g Protein

0g Fat

1g Fibre

Tomatoes, Cherry
40g, 4 small

1g Carbs

9 Cals

½ 5-a-day

1g Protein

0g Fat

1g Fibre

Tomatoes, Cherry
80g, 8 small

3g Carbs

18 Cals

1 5-a-day

1g Protein

2g Fat

0g SatFat

1g Fibre

Tomato, Sun-dried (in oil)
20g, drained

2g Carbs

35 Cals

0 5-a-day

2g Protein

5g Fat

1g SatFat

3g Fibre

Tomato, Sun-dried (in oil)
40g, drained

3g Carbs

69 Cals

0 5-a-day

1g Protein

0g Fat

0g Fibre

Watercress
20g, large handful

0g Carbs

4 Cals

0 5-a-day

1g Protein

0g Fat

1g Fibre

Watercress
40g, 2 large handfuls

0g Carbs

9 Cals

½ 5-a-day

0g
Protein

0g
Fat

0g
Fibre

0g
Carbs

1
Cals

0
5-a-day

Basil
6 leaves

0g
Protein

0g
Fat

0g
Fibre

0g
Carbs

1
Cals

0
5-a-day

Coriander
large sprig

0g
Protein

0g
Fat

0g
Fibre

0g
Carbs

1
Cals

0
5-a-day

Mint
5 leaves

0g
Protein

0g
Fat

0g
Fibre

0g
Carbs

1
Cals

0
5-a-day

Parsley
large sprig

0g
Protein

0g
Fat

0g
Fibre

0g
Carbs

1
Cals

0
5-a-day

Rosemary
sprig

0g
Protein

0g
Fat

0g
Fibre

0g
Carbs

1
Cals

0
5-a-day

Thyme
sprig

0g
Protein

0g
Fat

0g
Fibre

Apple
40g, ¼ medium

5g
Carbs

20
Cals

½
5-a-day

0g
Protein

0g
Fat

1g
Fibre

Apple
80g, ½ medium

9g
Carbs

41
Cals

1
5-a-day

0g
Protein

0g
Fat

2g
Fibre

Blackberries
40g

2g
Carbs

10
Cals

½
5-a-day

1g
Protein

0g
Fat

3g
Fibre

Blackberries
80g

4g
Carbs

20
Cals

1
5-a-day

0g
Protein

0g
Fat

1g
Fibre

Blueberries
40g

4g
Carbs

16
Cals

½
5-a-day

1g
Protein

0g
Fat

1g
Fibre

Blueberries
80g

7g
Carbs

32
Cals

1
5-a-day

Figs
30g

0g
Protein

0g
Fat

1g
Fibre

3g
Carbs

13
Cals

0
5-a-day

Figs
60g

1g
Protein

0g
Fat

1g
Fibre

6g
Carbs

26
Cals

½
5-a-day

Galia Melon
40g

0g
Protein

0g
Fat

0g
Fibre

2g
Carbs

10
Cals

½
5-a-day

Galia Melon
80g

0g
Protein

0g
Fat

0g
Fibre

4g
Carbs

19
Cals

1
5-a-day

Grapefruit
40g, ⅙ medium, peeled

0g
Protein

0g
Fat

1g
Fibre

3g
Carbs

12
Cals

½
5-a-day

Grapefruit
80g, ⅓ medium, peeled

1g
Protein

0g
Fat

1g
Fibre

5g
Carbs

24
Cals

1
5-a-day

0g Protein			
0g Fat	*Grapes* 40g		
0g Fibre	6g Carbs	25 Cals	½ 5-a-day

1g Protein			
0g Fat	*Grapes* 80g		
1g Fibre	12g Carbs	50 Cals	1 5-a-day

0g Protein			
0g Fat	*Lemon Peel* 3g		
0g Fibre	0g Carbs	1 Cals	0 5-a-day

0g Protein			
0g Fat	*Lemon Peel* 6g		
1g Fibre	1g Carbs	3 Cals	0 5-a-day

0g Protein			
0g Fat	*Mango* 40g, ¼ medium		
1g Fibre	6g Carbs	23 Cals	½ 5-a-day

1g Protein			
0g Fat	*Mango* 80g, ½ medium		
3g Fibre	11g Carbs	46 Cals	1 5-a-day

Nectarine
60g, destoned

1g Protein
0g Fat
1g Fibre
5g Carbs
24 Cals
½ 5-a-day

Nectarine
120g, destoned

2g Protein
0g Fat
2g Fibre
11g Carbs
48 Cals
1 5-a-day

Orange
40g, ⅙ medium, peeled

0g Protein
0g Fat
0g Fibre
3g Carbs
14 Cals
½ 5-a-day

Orange
80g, ⅓ medium, peeled

1g Protein
0g Fat
1g Fibre
7g Carbs
29 Cals
1 5-a-day

Peach
70g, destoned

1g Protein
0g Fat
1g Fibre
5g Carbs
23 Cals
½ 5-a-day

Peach
140g, destoned

1g Protein
0g Fat
3g Fibre
11g Carbs
46 Cals
1 5-a-day

0g Protein

Pear
40g, cored

0g Fat

1g Fibre

4g Carbs

17 Cals

½ 5-a-day

0g Protein

Pear
80g, cored

0g Fat

2g Fibre

9g Carbs

34 Cals

1 5-a-day

0g Protein

Pineapple
40g

0g Fat

1g Fibre

4g Carbs

16 Cals

½ 5-a-day

0g Protein

Pineapple
80g

0g Fat

1g Fibre

8g Carbs

33 Cals

1 5-a-day

0g Protein

Pomegranate Seeds
20g, 1 heaped tbsp

0g Fat

1g Fibre

3g Carbs

17 Cals

0 5-a-day

1g Protein

Pomegranate Seeds
40g, 2 heaped tbsp

0g Fat

1g Fibre

6g Carbs

34 Cals

½ 5-a-day

1g Protein
0g Fat
1g Fibre

Raspberries
40g

2g Carbs
10 Cals
½ 5-a-day

1g Protein
0g Fat
3g Fibre

Raspberries
80g

4g Carbs
20 Cals
1 5-a-day

0g Protein
0g Fat
2g Fibre

Strawberries
40g

2g Carbs
12 Cals
½ 5-a-day

0g Protein
0g Fat
3g Fibre

Strawberries
80g

5g Carbs
24 Cals
1 5-a-day

0g Protein
0g Fat
0g Fibre

Watermelon
40g

3g Carbs
12 Cals
½ 5-a-day

0g Protein
0g Fat
0g Fibre

Watermelon
80g

6g Carbs
25 Cals
1 5-a-day

Apricots
15g

1g Protein
0g Fat
2g Fibre
7g Carbs
28 Cals
½ 5-a-day

Apricots
30g

1g Protein
0g Fat
3g Fibre
13g Carbs
56 Cals
1 5-a-day

Cranberries
15g, 1 heaped tbsp

0g Protein
0g Fat
1g Fibre
12g Carbs
51 Cals
½ 5-a-day

Cranberries
30g, 2 heaped tbsp

0g Protein
0g Fat
1g Fibre
24g Carbs
102 Cals
1 5-a-day

Figs
15g

1g Protein
0g Fat
2g Fibre
8g Carbs
34 Cals
½ 5-a-day

Figs
30g

1g Protein
0g Fat
3g Fibre
16g Carbs
68 Cals
1 5-a-day

Goji Berries
3g, 1 tsp

0g Protein
0g Fat
0g Fibre
2g Carbs
10 Cals
0 5-a-day

Goji Berries
8g, 1 tbsp

1g Protein
0g Fat
1g Fibre
5g Carbs
26 Cals
0 5-a-day

Raisins
15g, 1 heaped tbsp

0g Protein
0g Fat
0g Fibre
10g Carbs
41 Cals
½ 5-a-day

Raisins
30g, 2 heaped tbsp

1g Protein
0g Fat
1g Fibre
21g Carbs
82 Cals
1 5-a-day

Sultanas
15g, 1 heaped tbsp

0g Protein
0g Fat
0g Fibre
10g Carbs
41 Cals
½ 5-a-day

Sultanas
30g, 2 heaped tbsp

1g Protein
0g Fat
1g Fibre
21g Carbs
83 Cals
1 5-a-day

Beef, Sirloin
100g, fried

- 27g Protein
- 14g Fat
- 6g SatFat
- 0g Fibre
- 0g Carbs
- 233 Cals
- 0 5-a-day

Beef, Sirloin
200g, fried

- 54g Protein
- 28g Fat
- 12g SatFat
- 0g Fibre
- 0g Carbs
- 466 Cals
- 0 5-a-day

Bacon
18g, grilled

- 4g Protein
- 4g Fat
- 1g SatFat
- 0g Fibre
- 0g Carbs
- 52 Cals
- 0 5-a-day

Bacon
36g, grilled

- 8g Protein
- 8g Fat
- 3g SatFat
- 0g Fibre
- 0g Carbs
- 103 Cals
- 0 5-a-day

Chicken Breast (no skin)
100g, grilled

- 32g Protein
- 2g Fat
- 1g SatFat
- 0g Fibre
- 0g Carbs
- 148 Cals
- 0 5-a-day

Chicken Breast (no skin)
200g, grilled

- 64g Protein
- 4g Fat
- 1g SatFat
- 0g Fibre
- 0g Carbs
- 296 Cals
- 0 5-a-day

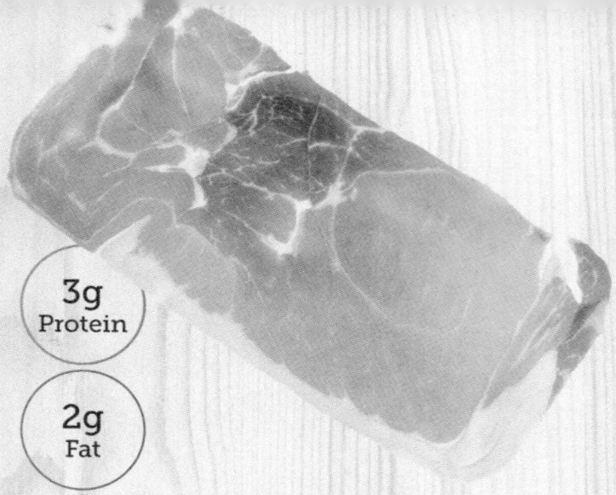

Parma Ham
12g

3g Protein
2g Fat
1g SatFat
0g Fibre
0g Carbs
27 Cals
0 5-a-day

Parma Ham
24g

7g Protein
3g Fat
1g SatFat
0g Fibre
0g Carbs
54 Cals
0 5-a-day

Chorizo
25g

6g Protein
8g Fat
3g SatFat
0g Fibre
1g Carbs
99 Cals
0 5-a-day

Chorizo
50g

12g Protein
16g Fat
6g SatFat
1g Fibre
1g Carbs
198 Cals
0 5-a-day

Turkey Breast
100g, grilled

35g Protein
2g Fat
1g SatFat
0g Fibre
0g Carbs
155 Cals
0 5-a-day

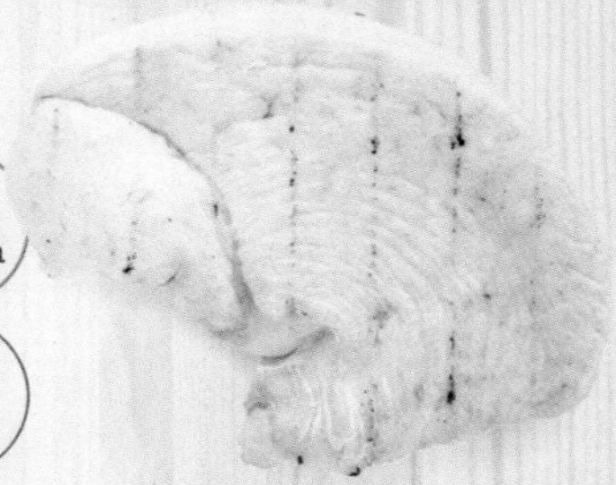

Turkey Breast
200g, grilled

70g Protein
3g Fat
1g SatFat
0g Fibre
0g Carbs
310 Cals
0 5-a-day

1g Protein

0g Fat

0g Fibre

Anchovies (tinned in oil)
4g, drained

0g Carbs · **8** Cals · **0** 5-a-day

3g Protein

1g Fat

0g Fibre

Anchovies (tinned in oil)
12g, drained

0g Carbs · **23** Cals · **0** 5-a-day

9g Protein

0g Fat

0g Fibre

Crab (tinned in brine)
50g, drained

0g Carbs · **39** Cals · **0** 5-a-day

18g Protein

1g Fat

0g Fibre

Crab (tinned in brine)
100g, drained

0g Carbs · **77** Cals · **0** 5-a-day

8g Protein

10g Fat

2g SatFat

0g Fibre

Mackerel
40g, smoked

0g Carbs · **120** Cals · **0** 5-a-day

16g Protein

18g Fat

4g SatFat

0g Fibre

Mackerel
75g, smoked

0g Carbs · **226** Cals · **0** 5-a-day

11g Protein

1g Fat

0g Fibre

Prawns
70g

0g Carbs

49 Cals

0 5-a-day

15g Protein

1g Fat

0g Fibre

Prawns
100g

0g Carbs

70 Cals

0 5-a-day

11g Protein

0g Fat

0g Fibre

King Prawns
70g

0g Carbs

48 Cals

0 5-a-day

16g Protein

0g Fat

0g Fibre

King Prawns
100g

0g Carbs

68 Cals

0 5-a-day

16g Protein

7g Fat

2g SatFat

0g Fibre

Salmon
60g, baked

0g Carbs

129 Cals

0 5-a-day

33g Protein

15g Fat

3g SatFat

0g Fibre

Salmon
125g, baked

0g Carbs

269 Cals

0 5-a-day

Smoked Salmon
50g

13g Protein
4g Fat
1g SatFat
0g Fibre
1g Carbs
93 Cals
0 5-a-day

Smoked Salmon
100g

25g Protein
9g Fat
2g SatFat
0g Fibre
1g Carbs
186 Cals
0 5-a-day

Salmon (tinned in brine)
85g, drained

20g Protein
6g Fat
1g SatFat
0g Fibre
0g Carbs
136 Cals
0 5-a-day

Salmon (tinned in brine)
170g, drained

40g Protein
12g Fat
2g SatFat
0g Fibre
0g Carbs
272 Cals
0 5-a-day

Sardines (tinned in brine)
50g, drained

11g Protein
5g Fat
1g SatFat
0g Fibre
0g Carbs
85 Cals
0 5-a-day

Sardines (tinned in brine)
100g, drained

22g Protein
9g Fat
3g SatFat
0g Fibre
0g Carbs
170 Cals
0 5-a-day

13g
Protein

3g
Fat

1g
SatFat

0g
Fibre

Trout
60g, smoked

0g
Carbs

79
Cals

0
5-a-day

27g
Protein

6g
Fat

1g
SatFat

0g
Fibre

Trout
125g, smoked

0g
Carbs

164
Cals

0
5-a-day

17g
Protein

1g
Fat

0g
Fibre

Tuna (tinned in brine)
70g, drained

0g
Carbs

76
Cals

0
5-a-day

35g
Protein

1g
Fat

0g
Fibre

Tuna (tinned in brine)
140g, drained

0g
Carbs

153
Cals

0
5-a-day

12g
Protein

2g
Fat

0g
SatFat

0g
Fibre

Scallops
50g, fried

0g
Carbs

65
Cals

0
5-a-day

25g
Protein

3g
Fat

1g
SatFat

0g
Fibre

Scallops
100g, fried

0g
Carbs

130
Cals

0
5-a-day

Brie 25g

- 5g Protein
- 7g Fat
- 5g SatFat
- 0g Fibre
- 0g Carbs
- 86 Cals
- 0 5-a-day

Brie 50g

- 10g Protein
- 15g Fat
- 9g SatFat
- 0g Fibre
- 0g Carbs
- 172 Cals
- 0 5-a-day

Camembert 25g

- 5g Protein
- 6g Fat
- 4g SatFat
- 0g Fibre
- 0g Carbs
- 73 Cals
- 0 5-a-day

Camembert 50g

- 11g Protein
- 11g Fat
- 7g SatFat
- 0g Fibre
- 0g Carbs
- 145 Cals
- 0 5-a-day

Cheddar 25g

- 6g Protein
- 9g Fat
- 5g SatFat
- 0g Fibre
- 0g Carbs
- 104 Cals
- 0 5-a-day

Cheddar 50g

- 13g Protein
- 17g Fat
- 11g SatFat
- 0g Fibre
- 0g Carbs
- 208 Cals
- 0 5-a-day

Cottage Cheese 50g
- 5g Protein
- 3g Fat
- 2g SatFat
- 0g Fibre
- 2g Carbs
- 52 Cals
- 0 5-a-day

Cottage Cheese 100g
- 9g Protein
- 6g Fat
- 3g SatFat
- 0g Fibre
- 3g Carbs
- 103 Cals
- 0 5-a-day

Dolcelatte 25g
- 5g Protein
- 9g Fat
- 6g SatFat
- 0g Fibre
- 0g Carbs
- 99 Cals
- 0 5-a-day

Dolcelatte 50g
- 9g Protein
- 18g Fat
- 11g SatFat
- 0g Fibre
- 0g Carbs
- 197 Cals
- 0 5-a-day

Feta 25g
- 4g Protein
- 5g Fat
- 3g SatFat
- 0g Fibre
- 0g Carbs
- 63 Cals
- 0 5-a-day

Feta 50g
- 8g Protein
- 10g Fat
- 7g SatFat
- 0g Fibre
- 1g Carbs
- 125 Cals
- 0 5-a-day

Goat's Cheese 25g
- 5g Protein
- 6g Fat
- 4g SatFat
- 0g Fibre
- 0g Carbs
- 80 Cals
- 0 5-a-day

Goat's Cheese 50g
- 11g Protein
- 13g Fat
- 9g SatFat
- 0g Fibre
- 1g Carbs
- 160 Cals
- 0 5-a-day

Halloumi 25g
- 6g Protein
- 6g Fat
- 4g SatFat
- 0g Fibre
- 0g Carbs
- 78 Cals
- 0 5-a-day

Halloumi 50g
- 12g Protein
- 12g Fat
- 8g SatFat
- 0g Fibre
- 1g Carbs
- 157 Cals
- 0 5-a-day

Mozzarella 25g
- 5g Protein
- 5g Fat
- 3g SatFat
- 0g Fibre
- 0g Carbs
- 64 Cals
- 0 5-a-day

Mozzarella 50g
- 9g Protein
- 10g Fat
- 7g SatFat
- 0g Fibre
- 0g Carbs
- 129 Cals
- 0 5-a-day

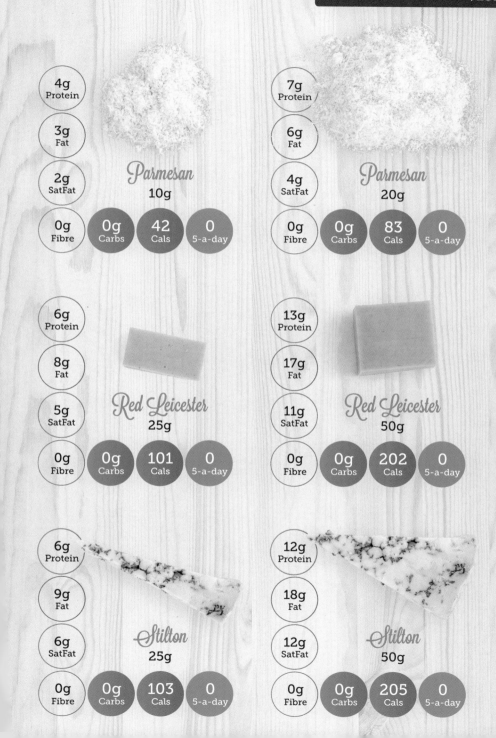

Parmesan
10g

4g Protein
3g Fat
2g SatFat
0g Fibre
0g Carbs
42 Cals
0 5-a-day

Parmesan
20g

7g Protein
6g Fat
4g SatFat
0g Fibre
0g Carbs
83 Cals
0 5-a-day

Red Leicester
25g

6g Protein
8g Fat
5g SatFat
0g Fibre
0g Carbs
101 Cals
0 5-a-day

Red Leicester
50g

13g Protein
17g Fat
11g SatFat
0g Fibre
0g Carbs
202 Cals
0 5-a-day

Stilton
25g

6g Protein
9g Fat
6g SatFat
0g Fibre
0g Carbs
103 Cals
0 5-a-day

Stilton
50g

12g Protein
18g Fat
12g SatFat
0g Fibre
0g Carbs
205 Cals
0 5-a-day

8g Protein
6g Fat
2g SatFat
0g Fibre

Egg
60g, 1 egg, boiled

0g Carbs
86 Cals
0 5-a-day

17g Protein
12g Fat
3g SatFat
0g Fibre

Egg
120g, 2 eggs, boiled

0g Carbs
172 Cals
0 5-a-day

10g Protein
2g Fat
1g SatFat
5g Fibre

Quorn Chicken Pieces
75g

1g Carbs
72 Cals
0 5-a-day

21g Protein
4g Fat
2g SatFat
10g Fibre

Quorn Chicken Pieces
150g

2g Carbs
144 Cals
0 5-a-day

9g Protein
7g Fat
1g SatFat
1g Fibre

Tofu
40g, fried

1g Carbs
104 Cals
0 5-a-day

19g Protein
14g Fat
2g SatFat
1g Fibre

Tofu
80g, fried

2g Carbs
209 Cals
0 5-a-day

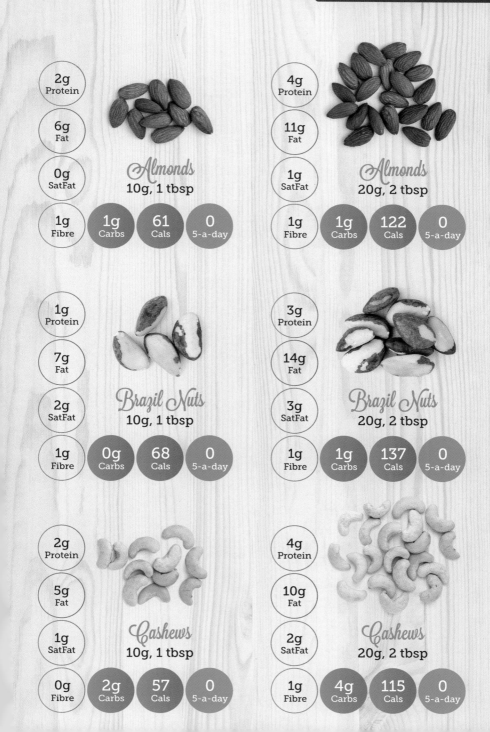

Almonds
10g, 1 tbsp

2g Protein
6g Fat
0g SatFat
1g Fibre
1g Carbs
61 Cals
0 5-a-day

Almonds
20g, 2 tbsp

4g Protein
11g Fat
1g SatFat
1g Fibre
1g Carbs
122 Cals
0 5-a-day

Brazil Nuts
10g, 1 tbsp

1g Protein
7g Fat
2g SatFat
1g Fibre
0g Carbs
68 Cals
0 5-a-day

Brazil Nuts
20g, 2 tbsp

3g Protein
14g Fat
3g SatFat
1g Fibre
1g Carbs
137 Cals
0 5-a-day

Cashews
10g, 1 tbsp

2g Protein
5g Fat
1g SatFat
0g Fibre
2g Carbs
57 Cals
0 5-a-day

Cashews
20g, 2 tbsp

4g Protein
10g Fat
2g SatFat
1g Fibre
4g Carbs
115 Cals
0 5-a-day

1g Protein
6g Fat
0g SatFat
1g Fibre

Hazelnuts
10g, 1 tbsp

1g Carbs
65 Cals
0 5-a-day

3g Protein
13g Fat
1g SatFat
1g Fibre

Hazelnuts
20g, 2 tbsp

1g Carbs
130 Cals
0 5-a-day

3g Protein
5g Fat
1g SatFat
1g Fibre

Peanuts
10g, 1 tbsp

1g Carbs
56 Cals
0 5-a-day

5g Protein
9g Fat
2g SatFat
1g Fibre

Peanuts
20g, 2 tbsp

3g Carbs
113 Cals
0 5-a-day

1g Protein
7g Fat
1g SatFat
1g Fibre

Pecans
10g, 1 tbsp

1g Carbs
69 Cals
0 5-a-day

2g Protein
14g Fat
1g SatFat
1g Fibre

Pecans
20g, 2 tbsp

1g Carbs
138 Cals
0 5-a-day

Pine Nuts
10g, 1 tbsp

1g Protein
7g Fat
0g SatFat
0g Fibre
0g Carbs
69 Cals
0 5-a-day

Pine Nuts
20g, 2 tbsp

3g Protein
14g Fat
1g SatFat
1g Fibre
1g Carbs
138 Cals
0 5-a-day

Pistachios
10g, 1 tbsp

2g Protein
6g Fat
1g SatFat
1g Fibre
1g Carbs
60 Cals
0 5-a-day

Pistachios
20g, 2 tbsp

4g Protein
11g Fat
1g SatFat
1g Fibre
2g Carbs
120 Cals
0 5-a-day

Walnuts
10g, 1 tbsp

1g Protein
7g Fat
1g SatFat
0g Fibre
0g Carbs
69 Cals
0 5-a-day

Walnuts
20g, 2 tbsp

3g Protein
14g Fat
2g SatFat
1g Fibre
1g Carbs
138 Cals
0 5-a-day

2g Protein
5g Fat
1g SatFat
1g Fibre

Pumpkin Seeds
10g, 1 tbsp

2g Carbs · 57 Cals · 0 5-a-day

5g Protein
9g Fat
1g SatFat
1g Fibre

Pumpkin Seeds
20g, 2 tbsp

3g Carbs · 113 Cals · 0 5-a-day

1g Protein
2g Fat
0g SatFat
0g Fibre

Sesame Seeds
3g, ½ tsp

0g Carbs · 18 Cals · 0 5-a-day

1g Protein
3g Fat
1g SatFat
1g Fibre

Sesame Seeds
5g, 1 tsp

0g Carbs · 30 Cals · 0 5-a-day

2g Protein
5g Fat
1g SatFat
1g Fibre

Sunflower Seeds
10g, 1 tbsp

2g Carbs · 58 Cals · 0 5-a-day

4g Protein
10g Fat
1g SatFat
2g Fibre

Sunflower Seeds
20g, 2 tbsp

4g Carbs · 115 Cals · 0 5-a-day

3g Protein

1g Fat

1g Fibre

Basmati Rice (cooked)
100g

27g Carbs | **117** Cals | **0** 5-a-day

6g Protein

1g Fat

1g Fibre

Basmati Rice (cooked)
200g

53g Carbs | **234** Cals | **0** 5-a-day

4g Protein

1g Fat

2g Fibre

Brown Rice (cooked)
100g

29g Carbs | **132** Cals | **0** 5-a-day

7g Protein

2g Fat

3g Fibre

Brown Rice (cooked)
200g

58g Carbs | **264** Cals | **0** 5-a-day

5g Protein

1g Fat

3g Fibre

Wild Rice (cooked)
100g

32g Carbs | **145** Cals | **0** 5-a-day

11g Protein

1g Fat

5g Fibre

Wild Rice (cooked)
200g

63g Carbs | **290** Cals | **0** 5-a-day

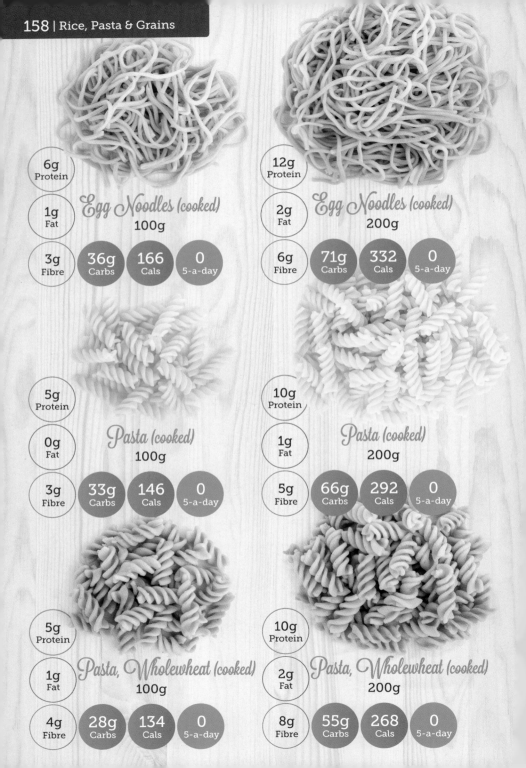

6g Protein

1g Fat

3g Fibre

Egg Noodles (cooked)
100g

36g Carbs | **166** Cals | **0** 5-a-day

12g Protein

2g Fat

6g Fibre

Egg Noodles (cooked)
200g

71g Carbs | **332** Cals | **0** 5-a-day

5g Protein

0g Fat

3g Fibre

Pasta (cooked)
100g

33g Carbs | **146** Cals | **0** 5-a-day

10g Protein

1g Fat

5g Fibre

Pasta (cooked)
200g

66g Carbs | **292** Cals | **0** 5-a-day

5g Protein

1g Fat

4g Fibre

Pasta, Wholewheat (cooked)
100g

28g Carbs | **134** Cals | **0** 5-a-day

10g Protein

2g Fat

8g Fibre

Pasta, Wholewheat (cooked)
200g

55g Carbs | **268** Cals | **0** 5-a-day

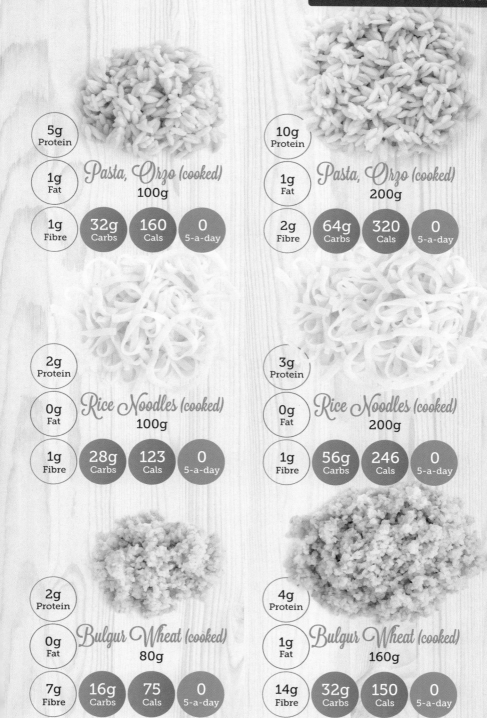

Pasta, Orzo (cooked)
100g

- 5g Protein
- 1g Fat
- 1g Fibre
- 32g Carbs
- 160 Cals
- 0 5-a-day

Pasta, Orzo (cooked)
200g

- 10g Protein
- 1g Fat
- 2g Fibre
- 64g Carbs
- 320 Cals
- 0 5-a-day

Rice Noodles (cooked)
100g

- 2g Protein
- 0g Fat
- 1g Fibre
- 28g Carbs
- 123 Cals
- 0 5-a-day

Rice Noodles (cooked)
200g

- 3g Protein
- 0g Fat
- 1g Fibre
- 56g Carbs
- 246 Cals
- 0 5-a-day

Bulgur Wheat (cooked)
80g

- 2g Protein
- 0g Fat
- 7g Fibre
- 16g Carbs
- 75 Cals
- 0 5-a-day

Bulgur Wheat (cooked)
160g

- 4g Protein
- 1g Fat
- 14g Fibre
- 32g Carbs
- 150 Cals
- 0 5-a-day

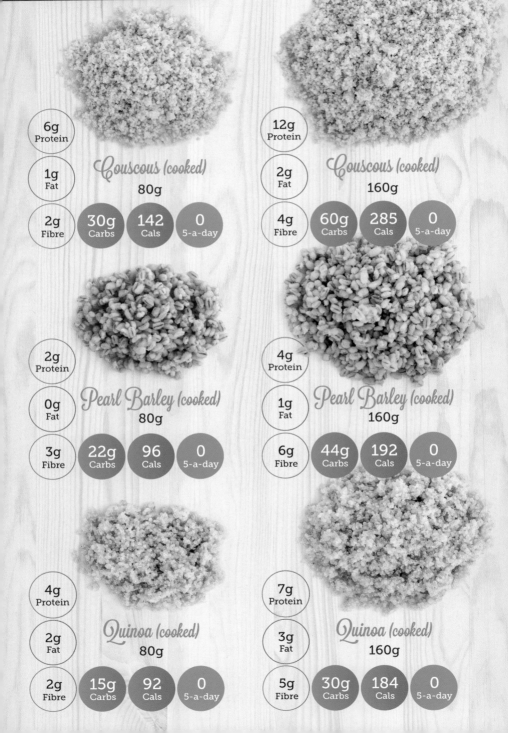

Couscous *(cooked)*
80g

6g Protein
1g Fat
2g Fibre
30g Carbs
142 Cals
0 5-a-day

Couscous *(cooked)*
160g

12g Protein
2g Fat
4g Fibre
60g Carbs
285 Cals
0 5-a-day

Pearl Barley *(cooked)*
80g

2g Protein
0g Fat
3g Fibre
22g Carbs
96 Cals
0 5-a-day

Pearl Barley *(cooked)*
160g

4g Protein
1g Fat
6g Fibre
44g Carbs
192 Cals
0 5-a-day

Quinoa *(cooked)*
80g

4g Protein
2g Fat
2g Fibre
15g Carbs
92 Cals
0 5-a-day

Quinoa *(cooked)*
160g

7g Protein
3g Fat
5g Fibre
30g Carbs
184 Cals
0 5-a-day

5g Protein

2g Fat

0g SatFat

Ciabatta
50g

2g Fibre | **26g** Carbs | **136** Cals | **0** 5-a-day

10g Protein

4g Fat

1g SatFat

Ciabatta
100g

3g Fibre | **52g** Carbs | **271** Cals | **0** 5-a-day

2g Protein

2g Fat

Croutons
15g

1g Fibre | **10g** Carbs | **66** Cals | **0** 5-a-day

4g Protein

4g Fat

Croutons
30g

1g Fibre | **20g** Carbs | **132** Cals | **0** 5-a-day

5g Protein

2g Fat

0g SatFat

Bread Roll (wholemeal)
50g

3g Fibre | **23g** Carbs | **122** Cals | **0** 5-a-day

8g Protein

2g Fat

1g SatFat

Bread Roll (wholemeal)
75g

4g Fibre | **35g** Carbs | **183** Cals | **0** 5-a-day

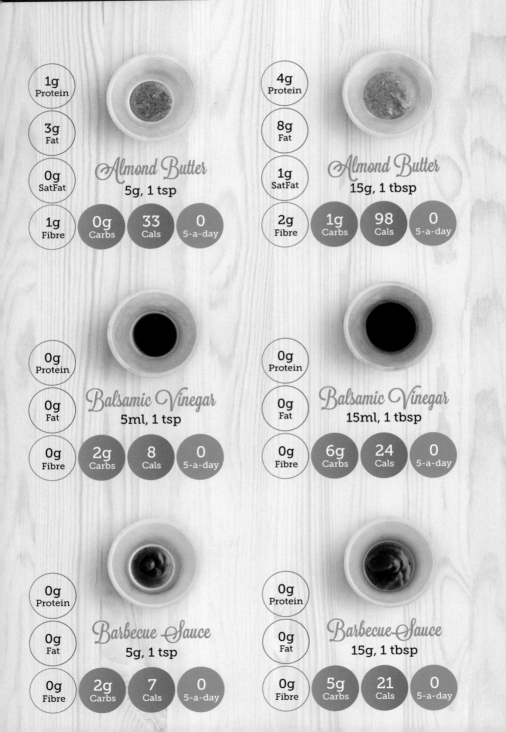

1g Protein
3g Fat
0g SatFat
1g Fibre

Almond Butter
5g, 1 tsp

0g Carbs
33 Cals
0 5-a-day

4g Protein
8g Fat
1g SatFat
2g Fibre

Almond Butter
15g, 1 tbsp

1g Carbs
98 Cals
0 5-a-day

0g Protein
0g Fat
0g Fibre

Balsamic Vinegar
5ml, 1 tsp

2g Carbs
8 Cals
0 5-a-day

0g Protein
0g Fat
0g Fibre

Balsamic Vinegar
15ml, 1 tbsp

6g Carbs
24 Cals
0 5-a-day

0g Protein
0g Fat
0g Fibre

Barbecue Sauce
5g, 1 tsp

2g Carbs
7 Cals
0 5-a-day

0g Protein
0g Fat
0g Fibre

Barbecue Sauce
15g, 1 tbsp

5g Carbs
21 Cals
0 5-a-day

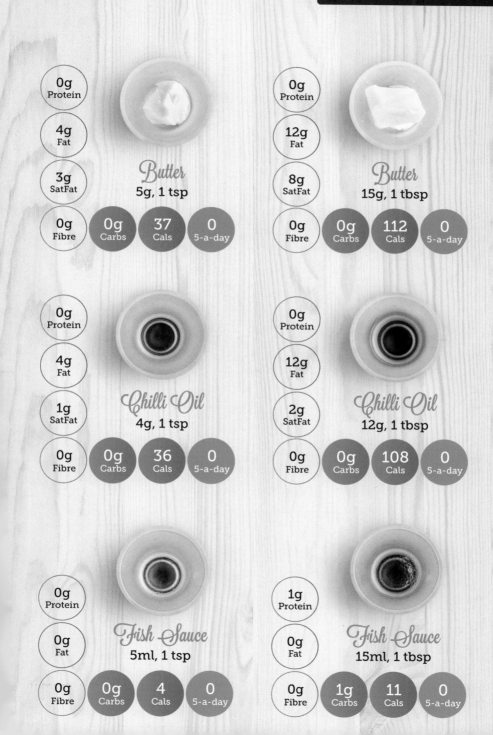

Butter
5g, 1 tsp

- 0g Protein
- 4g Fat
- 3g SatFat
- 0g Fibre
- 0g Carbs
- 37 Cals
- 0 5-a-day

Butter
15g, 1 tbsp

- 0g Protein
- 12g Fat
- 8g SatFat
- 0g Fibre
- 0g Carbs
- 112 Cals
- 0 5-a-day

Chilli Oil
4g, 1 tsp

- 0g Protein
- 4g Fat
- 1g SatFat
- 0g Fibre
- 0g Carbs
- 36 Cals
- 0 5-a-day

Chilli Oil
12g, 1 tbsp

- 0g Protein
- 12g Fat
- 2g SatFat
- 0g Fibre
- 0g Carbs
- 108 Cals
- 0 5-a-day

Fish Sauce
5ml, 1 tsp

- 0g Protein
- 0g Fat
- 0g Fibre
- 0g Carbs
- 4 Cals
- 0 5-a-day

Fish Sauce
15ml, 1 tbsp

- 1g Protein
- 0g Fat
- 0g Fibre
- 1g Carbs
- 11 Cals
- 0 5-a-day

Honey
6g, 1 tsp

0g Protein
0g Fat
0g Fibre
5g Carbs
17 Cals
0 5-a-day

Honey
18g, 1 tbsp

0g Protein
0g Fat
0g Fibre
14g Carbs
52 Cals
0 5-a-day

Horseradish Sauce
5g, 1 tsp

0g Protein
1g Fat
0g Fibre
1g Carbs
14 Cals
0 5-a-day

Horseradish Sauce
15g, 1 tbsp

0g Protein
3g Fat
0g Fibre
3g Carbs
42 Cals
0 5-a-day

Mayonnaise
5g, 1 tsp

0g Protein
4g Fat
0g SatFat
0g Fibre
0g Carbs
34 Cals
0 5-a-day

Mayonnaise
15g, 1 tbsp

0g Protein
11g Fat
1g SatFat
0g Fibre
0g Carbs
103 Cals
0 5-a-day

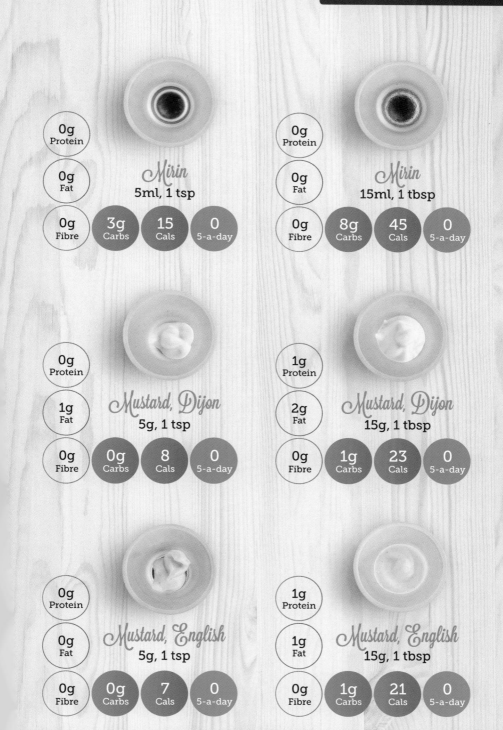

Mirin
5ml, 1 tsp

0g Protein
0g Fat
0g Fibre
3g Carbs
15 Cals
0 5-a-day

Mirin
15ml, 1 tbsp

0g Protein
0g Fat
0g Fibre
8g Carbs
45 Cals
0 5-a-day

Mustard, Dijon
5g, 1 tsp

0g Protein
1g Fat
0g Fibre
0g Carbs
8 Cals
0 5-a-day

Mustard, Dijon
15g, 1 tbsp

1g Protein
2g Fat
0g Fibre
1g Carbs
23 Cals
0 5-a-day

Mustard, English
5g, 1 tsp

0g Protein
0g Fat
0g Fibre
0g Carbs
7 Cals
0 5-a-day

Mustard, English
15g, 1 tbsp

1g Protein
1g Fat
0g Fibre
1g Carbs
21 Cals
0 5-a-day

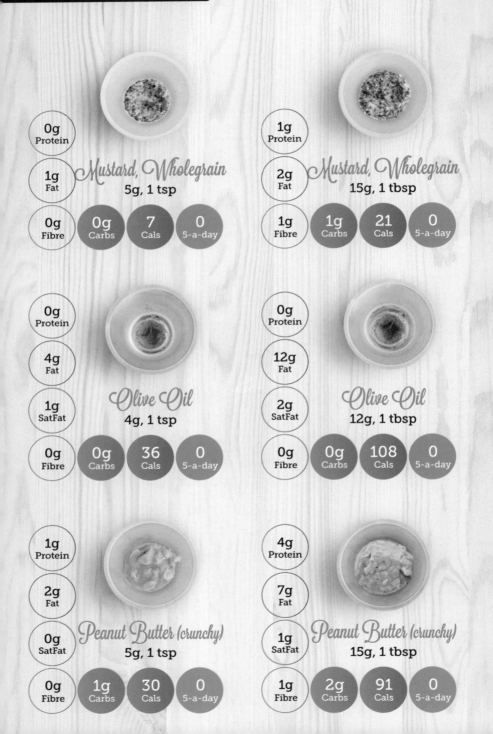

Mustard, Wholegrain
5g, 1 tsp

0g Protein
1g Fat
0g Fibre
0g Carbs
7 Cals
0 5-a-day

Mustard, Wholegrain
15g, 1 tbsp

1g Protein
2g Fat
1g Fibre
1g Carbs
21 Cals
0 5-a-day

Olive Oil
4g, 1 tsp

0g Protein
4g Fat
1g SatFat
0g Fibre
0g Carbs
36 Cals
0 5-a-day

Olive Oil
12g, 1 tbsp

0g Protein
12g Fat
2g SatFat
0g Fibre
0g Carbs
108 Cals
0 5-a-day

Peanut Butter (crunchy)
5g, 1 tsp

1g Protein
2g Fat
0g SatFat
0g Fibre
1g Carbs
30 Cals
0 5-a-day

Peanut Butter (crunchy)
15g, 1 tbsp

4g Protein
7g Fat
1g SatFat
1g Fibre
2g Carbs
91 Cals
0 5-a-day

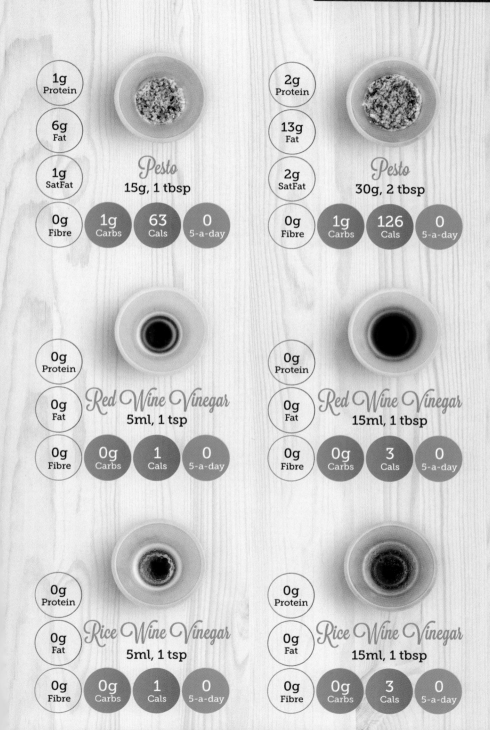

1g Protein
6g Fat
1g SatFat
0g Fibre

Pesto
15g, 1 tbsp

1g Carbs
63 Cals
0 5-a-day

2g Protein
13g Fat
2g SatFat
0g Fibre

Pesto
30g, 2 tbsp

1g Carbs
126 Cals
0 5-a-day

0g Protein
0g Fat
0g Fibre

Red Wine Vinegar
5ml, 1 tsp

0g Carbs
1 Cals
0 5-a-day

0g Protein
0g Fat
0g Fibre

Red Wine Vinegar
15ml, 1 tbsp

0g Carbs
3 Cals
0 5-a-day

0g Protein
0g Fat
0g Fibre

Rice Wine Vinegar
5ml, 1 tsp

0g Carbs
1 Cals
0 5-a-day

0g Protein
0g Fat
0g Fibre

Rice Wine Vinegar
15ml, 1 tbsp

0g Carbs
3 Cals
0 5-a-day

Satay Sauce
5g, 1 tsp

0g Protein
1g Fat
0g Fibre
1g Carbs
10 Cals
0 5-a-day

Satay Sauce
15g, 1 tbsp

1g Protein
2g Fat
0g Fibre
2g Carbs
29 Cals
0 5-a-day

Sesame Oil
4g, 1 tsp

0g Protein
4g Fat
1g SatFat
0g Fibre
0g Carbs
36 Cals
0 5-a-day

Sesame Oil
12g, 1 tbsp

0g Protein
12g Fat
2g SatFat
0g Fibre
0g Carbs
108 Cals
0 5-a-day

Soy Sauce
5ml, 1 tsp

0g Protein
0g Fat
0g Fibre
1g Carbs
4 Cals
0 5-a-day

Soy Sauce
15ml, 1 tbsp

0g Protein
0g Fat
0g Fibre
3g Carbs
12 Cals
0 5-a-day

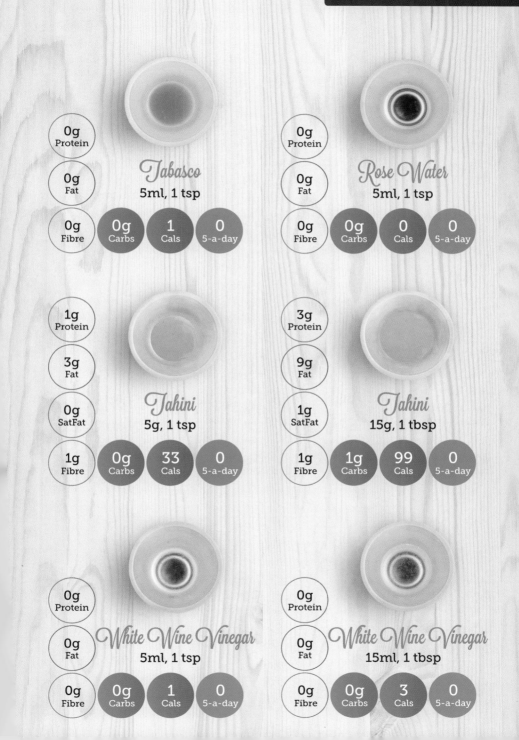

Tabasco
5ml, 1 tsp

0g Protein
0g Fat
0g Fibre
0g Carbs
1 Cals
0 5-a-day

Rose Water
5ml, 1 tsp

0g Protein
0g Fat
0g Fibre
0g Carbs
0 Cals
0 5-a-day

Tahini
5g, 1 tsp

1g Protein
3g Fat
0g SatFat
1g Fibre
0g Carbs
33 Cals
0 5-a-day

Tahini
15g, 1 tbsp

3g Protein
9g Fat
1g SatFat
1g Fibre
1g Carbs
99 Cals
0 5-a-day

White Wine Vinegar
5ml, 1 tsp

0g Protein
0g Fat
0g Fibre
0g Carbs
1 Cals
0 5-a-day

White Wine Vinegar
15ml, 1 tbsp

0g Protein
0g Fat
0g Fibre
0g Carbs
3 Cals
0 5-a-day

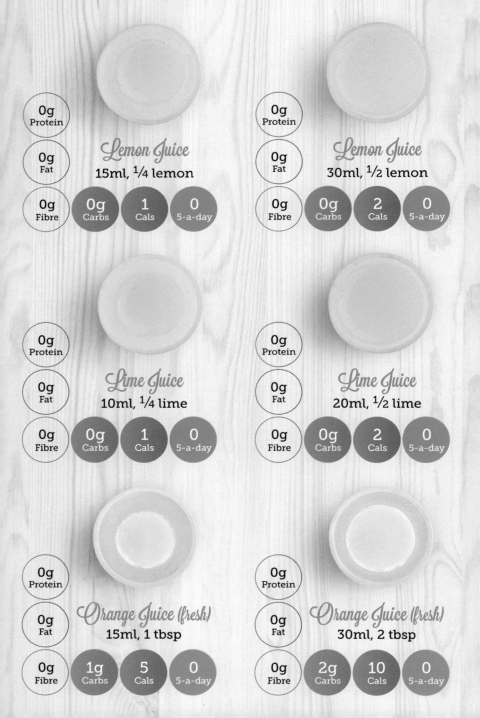

Lemon Juice
15ml, ¼ lemon

0g Protein
0g Fat
0g Fibre
0g Carbs
1 Cals
0 5-a-day

Lemon Juice
30ml, ½ lemon

0g Protein
0g Fat
0g Fibre
0g Carbs
2 Cals
0 5-a-day

Lime Juice
10ml, ¼ lime

0g Protein
0g Fat
0g Fibre
0g Carbs
1 Cals
0 5-a-day

Lime Juice
20ml, ½ lime

0g Protein
0g Fat
0g Fibre
0g Carbs
2 Cals
0 5-a-day

Orange Juice (fresh)
15ml, 1 tbsp

0g Protein
0g Fat
0g Fibre
1g Carbs
5 Cals
0 5-a-day

Orange Juice (fresh)
30ml, 2 tbsp

0g Protein
0g Fat
0g Fibre
2g Carbs
10 Cals
0 5-a-day

0g Protein
2g Fat
2g SatFat
0g Fibre
1g Carbs
24 Cals
0 5-a-day

Crème Fraîche (half fat)
15g, 1 tbsp

1g Protein
5g Fat
3g SatFat
0g Fibre
1g Carbs
49 Cals
0 5-a-day

Crème Fraîche (half fat)
30g, 2 tbsp

1g Protein
0g Fat
0g Fibre
1g Carbs
8 Cals
0 5-a-day

Greek Yogurt (fat free)
15g, 1 tbsp

2g Protein
0g Fat
0g Fibre
2g Carbs
16 Cals
0 5-a-day

Greek Yogurt (fat free)
30g, 2 tbsp

1g Protein
0g Fat
0g Fibre
1g Carbs
8 Cals
0 5-a-day

Natural Yogurt (fat free)
15g, 1 tbsp

2g Protein
0g Fat
0g Fibre
2g Carbs
16 Cals
0 5-a-day

Natural Yogurt (fat free)
30g, 2 tbsp

Salad Index

Ingredient Index